Resilience Enhancement For The Resident Physician

by
Edward Messner, M.D.

Associate Clinical Professor of Psychiatry
Harvard Medical School
Psychiatrist
Massachusetts General Hospital
Boston, Massachusetts 02114

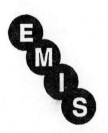

Essential Medical Information Systems, Inc.
P.O. Box 1607
Durant, OK 74702

Published by
Essential Medical Information Systems, Inc.
P.O. Box 1607
Durant, OK 74702

For Phone Orders Call:
1-800-225-0694
FAX Your Order
405/924-9414

ISBN: 0-929240-57-X

—Disclaimer—

The ideas and opinions expressed in this book are the author's and are not necessarily shared by any organization with which he is affiliated.

Published in the United States of America

to
Marie Messner

—TABLE OF CONTENTS—

—TABLES—

Introduction

Internship has been known within the medical profession for many decades as a grueling, inundating, transforming experience. It has aroused intense feelings, favorable and unfavorable, among the physicians who have lived and worked through it. Interns have inspired novels and dramas. In recent years, increasing concern has arisen within the medical profession and in lay communities that internship and the immediately succeeding years of training have become increasingly stressful, perhaps to a seriously destructive degree. Medical school faculties, as well as hospital staffs, have experienced concern and have debated the rigorous experience endured by recent graduates of medical schools. The challenges of sleep deprivation and stints of continuous work extending far beyond 24 hours have raised questions among senior physicians, educators, psychologists and others, about whether this degree of strenuousness impairs medical education. Concerned groups of patients, third party payers, and other business interests have become concerned about whether these programs have become so harsh that they have engendered hardness and dysphoria among young physicians that ultimately detracts from the effective and compassionate practice of medicine.

In recent years, public concern about the intensity of the training experience for house officers has increased following a malpractice suit in New York City provoked by the death of a young woman who had been treated by house officers at a teaching hospital. The Libby Zion Case gained wide publicity and intensified the debate within the medical profession about the efficacy of internship and residency; what needed to be done to prevent harm to patients; and how to reduce exposure to malpractice suits of this kind.

Even prior to this tragic case, studies had been conducted to determine which of the many features of internship and residency were stressful; to what extent did they impair the functioning of the resident; to what extent did they interfere with optimal patient care; and some of the studies even investigated the effects on the personal lives, family lives, and attitudes, including compassion, of the young physicians. Many suggestions have been made as a result of these studies about how postgraduate medical training, especially internship, can be made more humane for the trainee, while retaining the best educational aspects of intense patient care. These studies and proposals have engendered considerable debate within the medical profession and in the public press, as well as in legislatures and among insurance companies and others concerned about the financing of medical care and training. Much has been published as a result of these studies and debates.

Most of the recommendations for changes in postgraduate medical education have been institutional. That is, they have recommended changes that could be brought about through modifications in curricula, in hospital procedures and in medical school faculty requirements, as well as in requirements of specialty boards. Relatively little has been published about what individual medical students, interns and residents can do to fortify themselves in the face of the empowering but painful transition of postgraduate medical training. This book offers suggestions and procedures that individuals might find useful in overcoming the demands and threats of internship while enhancing the opportunities to develop maturity as individuals and as physicians.

Medical students and interns are exceptionally competent, resourceful people. For generations, the large majority have proven themselves capable of surmounting the rigors of postgraduate medical training and developing into admirable physicians and surgeons. We are not certain how many have suffered what degree of personal, attitudinal, familial or professional morbidity. Most, if not all, have adaptive capabilities that can be cultivated and extended to enable them to cope even more effectively if they are given some preparation and some direction. To provide such reinforcement is the aim of this book.

It is not intended as a substitute for institutional changes that will reduce the number of casualties among young physicians. In many of the studies, some of which are cited in the bibliography, the occurrence of depression, marital disruption, impairment of morale and reduction of idealism and compassion are well documented. The likelihood of impairment of patient care is a matter of great concern to many who have studied house officer training. Much needs to be done on the institutional level to reduce the unnecessarily demanding features of internship.

Such changes will probably continue to be made, but slowly and gradually. This slow pace will be related to opposition by medical faculties that want to preserve the best in teaching, and the best in opportunities for learning, some of which require intense and prolonged periods of work with patients. The rate of change in training conditions will also be slowed by economic considerations.While all of this is going on, many thousands of medical school graduates will enter internship and face the ravages of prolonged periods of sleeplessness, isolation from their families, accelerating pace, and intensity of responsibility. The suggestions included in this book are intended to help them to adapt to their conditions of work and training, and beyond that to learn and to grow, and to retain, or even enhance, their idealism and compassion for patients.

Apart from factors that could be modified by hospitals or medical schools, many potentially daunting tasks remain. Responsibility for clinical decisions that may affect patients profoundly; involvement in death, disability and tragedy on a nearly daily basis; contact with personally hazardous circumstances such as human immunovirus (HIV)-infected blood in traumatic emergencies—these are a few examples. Ethical dilemmas related to availability of treatment resources are added to the violence of drug-crazed patients and the frustrations inherent in caring for people who contribute behaviorally to their own cardiac or pulmonary disease with salt, fat or smoke.

Procedures such as mental rehearsal, directed fantasies and autohypnosis can be useful in enabling the intern to respond to these difficult tasks with more effectiveness and less personal erosion. The intern's own coping strategies can be winnowed, and other resources, such as family, friends, peers and elders can be recruited and enhanced. These and others are included among the suggestions contained in the chapters ahead.

Apart from the content and purpose of this work, two comments about the use of language need to be made. The first is my use of third person masculine pronouns when referring to both males and females. Much of this book is based upon experience and learning that I was privileged to gain over more than two decades of teaching medical students and residents. Nearly all of this was accomplished in small group, interactive, teaching situations like seminars and one-on-one, or one-on-two supervision.

Part of my experience also included psychotherapy which I provided for students, interns, residents and fully trained physicians over an even longer period of time. In the early drafts of much of this material, I used expressions like "him or her", "he or she" and "himself or herself" as I do in the seminars. In rereading that early draft material, I found it repetitious, tedious and cumbersome, qualities that my writing can ill afford. In giving it further thought, I recalled that in the teaching situations the use of the alternative masculine and feminine third person pronouns is interwoven with second person, as well as non-verbal communication: directing one's gaze or speech toward various members of the seminar group. These added variety to my comments, while retaining the clear message that my concern is directed to both women and men. This explanation may be cumbersome to some and insufficient to others, but it is how I came to revert to the traditional use of the masculine pronouns.

The second matter related to language is my use of the traditional term "intern", rather than the current reference to "first year resident", or "first post-graduate year" (PGY-1). The inclusion of interns under the heading of residents has much to be said for it, and in part is related to the increasing tendency of training programs to be continuous. Relatively few medical school graduates nowadays, at least in the United States, limit themselves to a single year of internship. Usually, new doctors will continue at the same institution to obtain specialty training.

I have retained the old term, "internship", partly because it is far more familiar than the PGY terminology. In part, also, there are some very special features to the first year of postgraduate training in terms of the onslaught of responsibility and alteration of the style of life that has profound emotional effects on the young physician. Although the first year of residency, or as it is now known, PGY-2, is only slightly less stressful in most instances, the transitional phenomena in the first year retain certain distinctions. The internship starts with a medical student who has earned the degree, doctor of medicine. Sometime during that year that student becomes a physician in terms of his inner view of himself (Please note that this is a use of "himself", when I clearly mean "himself or herself"). As difficult as the PGY-2 often is, the young physician by this time already feels like a doctor.

The main focus of the suggestions, ideas and procedures offered in the body of this work is the internship year.

The student who used some of these suggestions to prepare will probably be making the most effective use of what will be offered. Some of the procedures can be learned quickly and put into almost immediate practice. Therefore, they could be employed by young physicians already in their PGY 1, or in subsequent PGYs. Some of them can actually be employed well past their training years into the years of practice. This has been true of some of my colleagues, my physician patients, and I have employed many of them myself.

Many of the internal techniques are summarized in the tables. These can be used as guides or checklists. They are not intended to demean these complex emotional processes by oversimplification. The reader can enrich them with his own individual style and adapt them to his own unique personality and circumstances. For many, introduction of personally meaningful variants can make the procedures more effective and useful.

I offer the suggestions in this book to my young and future colleagues with the hope that they will do no harm; that they will fortify and strengthen; and that they will contribute something to the glorious privilege that medical practice can be.

Chapter 1

The Challenge of Internship and Residency

Building resilience for residency refers to a totality of personal preparedness for postgraduate medical training. It includes attitudes, academic preparation, physical vigor and emotional fortitude. This book will provide ideas and procedures to help the student or resident expand his capacity to adapt to postgraduate training.

The education and training that the student receives in medical school, in the vast majority of instances, will be adequate preparation academically for postgraduate training. Humanitarian attitudes, desires to help and to heal one's fellow human beings, are very likely present already in the student when he enrolls in medical school. Most of us who enter the profession of medicine are motivated, at least in part, to alleviate pain and to treat people suffering diseases and injuries.

Reactive Misanthropy

The intensely stressful nature of postgraduate medical training blunts that humane thrust in some interns and residents. This is manifested by attitudes and behavior exhibited by too many senior residents and attending physicians. They may be harsh with patients, dislike them, feel that patients are the enemy, people who impose more work on an overburdened doctor. Even some of the attending physicians and surgeons who participate in the training of medical students and residents seem to have lost much of their warmth and concern for patients. There is, instead, a kind of crusty defensiveness or outright hostility and contempt that more than a few exhibit about patients. Such misanthropic attitudes may evolve as a kind of self-protection in the face of the exhausting and stressful experiences of internship. Exposure to death, suffering, hostility from patients – including manipulation, ingratitude, and even physical threats – lead to distancing by the young physician. This may be intensified to the point of outright antagonism toward patients as a way of safeguarding the young physician's own feelings. Sometimes this kind of emotional self-protection may spread to include all patients, even those who are appreciative, respectful, pleasant and responsive to treatment.

In its more malignant forms, the antipathy that young physicians develop toward patients may spread to other relationships outside the professional. These may include fellow physicians, others in health care professions, and even close personal relationships. Students may have seen examples of senior residents embarrassing and humiliating junior residents and interns. They may even have experienced humiliation on rounds inflicted by senior residents or attending physicians.

Abuse of medical students is shamefully common. Carefully designed studies have revealed and documented its extensive prevalence in many forms. Physical, sexual, verbal and psychological abuse have been reported by numerous students. With publication of research conducted at several medical schools in the United States, the consciousness of the medical profession has been directed to this blight.

Measures for prevention and for institutional responses to episodes of abuse of medical students have been suggested. With time, some of them will probably be put into practice in many schools. Meanwhile, each student must learn to protect, soothe and heal himself and to find help on his own.

Many young physicians may allow the hostility they develop in the hospital to continue with them in the home. Marital disruption and divorce occur with substantial frequency during and in the years immediately following the completion of residency training. Many of these instances of marital disruption result from frustrations, deprivation and emotional pain carried home from the hospital.

The house officer may demean the concerns of the non-medical spouse. These may be shrugged off as being not as important as saving lives and relieving pain. The non-medical spouse may be distressed about the illness of a child or parent, or by loneliness in a strange community with few friends and very little support. Practical and financial concerns may also be minimized as being beneath the concern of the exhausted physician.

The intern may be too tired for empathic listening, reasonable conversation, sharing of household chores, recreation or even for sex. The physician may be irritable or self-absorbed as a result of the stressful and exhausting work that he must engage in at the hospital.

Other aspects of the maritally stressful nature of residency training include much time away from home and preoccupation with events too gruesome to describe to many who are not hospital professionals.

Preparatory Strengthening

My hope, in preparing this book, is to help prevent those adverse effects on the personalities and personal lives of young physicians. By calling attention to the stresses and to ways of meeting them in healthy and effective ways, the student might strengthen himself enough to withstand and to overcome whatever may come his way during house officer training. My hypothesis is that if the intern is well prepared emotionally, and has an effective repertoire of procedures for coping with these rigors, the adverse effects will be minimized. This does not negate the necessity for institutional reduction in the grinding demands imposed.

A parallel goal is to fortify the intern so he will be able to provide the most effective care for his patients. The intern's treatment of patients may then be less adversely affected by defensiveness, avoidance or the emotional and cognitive exhaustion that often accompanies physical exhaustion and deprivation of sleep.

Most medical students keep busy trying to learn medicine and to develop the clinical skills that are essential to future training and practice. Many do not devote much attention to consideration of the personal problems that house officer training will bring. Postgraduate training is known to be stressful and not pleasant to contemplate. Usually students consider the kind of training that they will get, the quality, the specialty, the particularly desirable residency programs. If they consider it at all, most assume that they will overcome the difficulties as they have overcome previous and current problems. In the vast majority of cases they are right. They will proceed into postgraduate training, accomplish it, and go on to practice.

As suggested earlier, the price of this success if often high. This book is intended to reduce the cost and to increase the benefit. The stresses of internship will be examined later in some detail. The following are a few examples of stresses briefly described.

Responsibility For Patient Care

Responsibility is the greatest difference between the house officer and the student. While the student is mainly responsible for learning, the intern is responsible for the care of the patient and its outcome. This is one of the gratifying challenges of medicine; so it is often a reward as well as a stress. Responsibility, of course, is shared by members of the team, by senior residents and attending physicians, but it is the intern who is usually identified as the patient's doctor. The pain comes when things go wrong.

Emergencies And Forty Hour Days

It is well known that the intern will have to deal with emergencies, extremely urgent tasks, and that he will be interrupted frequently, even while performing essential duties. The house officer will work exhaustively long hours: duty for more than twenty four hours, sometimes as many as forty or more hours, without significant interruption for rest, or even for meals. Tasks are extremely varied, and the intern will have to shift his attention and focus back and forth among diagnostic, therapeutic, laboratory and interpersonal functions with great rapidity. Great demands will be made on the intern's fund of knowledge, and he will be required to exhibit skill with relatively little practice. These requirements will not be simply of an academic nature but often practical and urgent in the immediate care of hospital patients. There will be intense and prolonged practical applications of information that he gathered in an academic atmosphere but will have to apply under conditions of pain, bleeding, distress and fear.

AIDS

In recent years, acquired immune deficiency syndrome (AIDS) has imposed enormous challenges to interns as it affects more and more of their patients. AIDS is a threat to the house officer, under some circumstances, and he must learn to cope with this hazard as well as to treat the patient. The undiagnosed carrier of the HIV is especially dangerous. Interns touch or are spattered with blood in emergency rooms, in surgery, and as result of accidents. Students are exposed similarly when drawing blood, placing intravenous lines, or drawing samples for arterial blood gases.

13

Malpractice Litigation

In the United States, a litigious attitude has intensified in the relationship between patient and physician. Malpractice suits have become increasingly common and create and an ominous cloud over specialties such as obstetrics and orthopaedics and extend to virtually every specialty of medicine. These threats are particularly present in the high risk and severe conditions that are treated in teaching hospitals. Extremely sick patients are admitted, and many opportunities arise for things to go wrong. When difficulties arise, not only is human suffering greater, but the possibility of legal action taken by the patient or his family increases.

The distinction between maloccurrence and malpractice has become blurred in the minds of patients, their families and the public at large. Americans and others have come to expect perfection and infallibility from scientific modern medicine. Unfortunately, a lawsuit, no matter how undeserved and irrationally motivated, can distress a young physician. It can be punitively burdensome, worrisome and disillusioning.

Ethical Choices

Another source of personal stress is the array of ethical dilemmas faced by interns. The young physician is forced to deal with situations in which patients need care but the facilities for providing such care are limited. Factors such as financial limitations, insufficient equipment, scarcity of blood or other essential supplies demand that someone make a decision: who will get the blood, who will not; who will get the scarce supplies, who will not; who will be hospitalized? Patients who may need to be treated in a hospital may not have insurance coverage. Increasingly, third party payers, including the Federal Government, set limits on how many days the patient may be kept in the hospital. These restrictions are often faced by interns at considerable emotional cost to themselves. If they allow themselves to contemplate the consequences of some of these decisions, the pain may be excruciating. If they overprotect themselves from such pain by distancing, denial, or other mechanisms of avoidance, they may toughen themselves to the point of callousness.

Considerable evidence exists that many interns and residents fall victim to substance abuse. Others become depressed beyond what would be expected of well educated, healthy, strong people like those who are able to complete medical school. More commonly, there is the embitterment and blunting of humanitarian impulses that lead to the misanthropy hinted at earlier. Disillusionment, impaired idealism, and a tendency toward self centeredness and severe materialism may result from exposure over months and years to such stresses.

Most of these problems are well known. They can be anticipated. Students can develop understanding of the difficult situations that they can expect to encounter and by thinking ahead, can prepare methods for overcoming them. Coping devices can be learned, developed and cultivated.

The hundreds of students and young physicians whom I have taught or treated have revealed what has worked effectively and what has not. It is my hope to pass that information on to the reader. Postgraduate training does not have to be debilitating. It can be strengthening and invigorating, despite the burdens it imposes. It can be a challenge to be mastered. One of the rewards is a strengthening of self-confidence and optimism. Another, and perhaps the greatest, is the opportunity to go on to practice medicine, which can be a life of quiet glory.

References

Adler R, Werner ER, Korsch B: Systematic study of four years of internship. Pediatrics 1980; 66:1000-1008.

Aoun H: When a house officer gets AIDS. N Eng J Med 1989; 321:693-696.

Arras JD: The fragile web of responsibility: AIDS and the duty to treat. Hastings Center Rep 1988; 18(2): Suppl: 10-20.

Asch DA, Parker RM: The Libby Zion Case: One step forward or two steps backward? N Engl J Med 1988; 318:771-775.

Barlow E: Rites of residency: New age stresses on the iron intern. Harvard Med Alumni Bull 1989; 62(3):36-41.

Bjorksten O, Sutherland S, Miller C, et al: Identification of medical student problems and comparison with those of other students. J Med Educ 1983; 58:759-767.

Blackwell B: Prevention of impairment among residents in training. JAMA 1986; 255:1177-1178.

Borenstein DB, Cook K: Impairment prevention in the training years: A new mental health program at UCLA. JAMA 1982; 247:2700-2703.

Bronner E: The foot soldiers of medicine. The Boston Sunday Globe Magazine, July 6, 1986.

Butterfield PS: The stress of residency: A review of the literature. Arch Intern Med 1988; 148:1428-1434.

Colford JM, McPhee SJ: The raveled sleeve of care: Managing the stresses of residency training. JAMA 1989; 261:890-894.

Cooke M, Sande MA: The HIV epidemic and training in internal medicine. N Engl J Med 1989; 321:1334-1338.

Cousins N: Internship: Preparation or hazing? JAMA 1981; 245:377.

Earle M: Physician Heal Thyself! Minneapolis, MN, Comp Care Publishers, 1989.

Fine SB: Resilience and human adaptability: Who rises above adversity? Am J Occup Therapy 1991;45:493-503.

Friedman RC, Bigger JT, Kornfeld DS: The intern and sleep loss. N Engl J Med 1971; 285:201-203.

Friedman RC, Kornfeld DS, Bigger TJ: Psychological problems associated with sleep deprivation in interns. J Med Educ 1973; 48:436-441.

Hardison JE: The house officer's changing world. N Engl J Med 1986; 314:1713-1715.

Hawkins MR, Vichick DA, Silsby HD et al: Sleep deprivation and performance of house officers. J Med Educ 1985; 60:530-535.

Hsu K, Dolan D: Primary prevention of physician impairment at the medical student level. Can J Psychiatry 1983; 28:415-416.

Internship: Physicians Respond to Norman Cousins. JAMA 1981; 246:2141-2144.

Keller KL, Koenig WJ: Management of stress and prevention of burnout in emergency physicians. Ann Emerg Med 1989;18:42-47.

Link RN, Feingold AR, Charap MH, et al: Concerns of medical and pediatric house officers about acquiring AIDS from their patients. Am J Public Health 1988; 78:455-459.

Lurie N, Rank B, Parenti C, et al: How do house officers spend their nights? A time study of internal medicine house staff on call. N Engl J Med 1989; 320:1673-1677.

McCall TB: The impact of long working hours on resident physicians. N Engl J Med 1988; 318:775-778.

McCall TB: Sleep deprivation and performance of residents. JAMA 1989; 261:859.

Wachter RM: The impact of the acquired immunodeficiency syndrome on medical residency training. N Engl J Med 1986; 314:177-180.

Chapter 2

Benefits of Mental Rehearsal

Anticipation and planning are key elements of rational living. Education provides its own immediate satisfactions, but training and learning are usually directed toward preparing one's self for future experience. Medical school is an outstanding example.

Mental rehearsal is a form of planning. It refers here to imagining in detail one's response to a set of circumstances that can be anticipated. From a psychological point of view, precise preparation for emotionally stressful situations can be highly rewarding. It enables an individual to practice in advance and in safety the adaptations that might be most effective for a stressful event: for example, the death of a patient.

Even after 39 years, I can still remember the first patient I saw die. It occurred on my course in physical diagnosis, our first experience on the hospital wards. The patient was an elderly woman, comatose, whose breathing simply stopped. In those days, we were not familiar with cardiopulmonary resuscitation, and nothing much was done. I saw her breathing, and then it stopped. My thoughts were that here is something that's irreversible. She was alive one moment, and then dead. She became a cadaver, like the one I had helped dissect the previous year in gross anatomy. It was an eerie experience. I felt strange and wondered to myself whether this was something that I would be able to endure.

I had no connection with that patient, except that she might have been someone whom I had been assigned to examine. Still, the memory remains even after all this time. It can be useful for students to think ahead to imagine that kind of experience, especially with the patient for whom the student will have some responsibility. By thinking ahead, the student might anticipate his emotional state and prepare for it.

Mental rehearsal is familiar in professional experience. Learning to perform physical examinations, venipunctures, or other procedures is enhanced if we practice it in imagination in addition to practicing it in fact.

When I first learned the various procedures for physical diagnosis, I was enthusiastic but anxious. It was hard for me to keep all of the procedures in mind in the order in which they were to be used. At one point, it dawned on me that the physical examination was to be conducted essentially from head to toe. Once that obvious concept penetrated, I was able to visualize the patient and to proceed in a relatively calm and orderly sequence.

Preparation For Clinical Emergencies

Medical school prepares us for things that may go wrong. We learn what can happen in the operating room that may be serious and life threatening. We study complications of illness and adverse reactions to drugs. Undesirable events that may occur in medical or surgical practice are reviewed, analyzed and anticipated. Corrective procedures and treatment are prepared. These are essential parts of clinical training in medical school. By learning what can go wrong and what can be done about it, we prepare competent professional responses to complications and emergencies.

In this spirit, physicians learn basic life support, advanced life support, intensive care, and coronary care procedures. Every clinical specialty has its own set of emergency procedures, and the house staff is trained and drilled in their use.

Preparation For Emotional Impacts

Similar preparation can be made for emotionally stressful events that we can anticipate in the course of postgraduate medical training. Intense human reactions to circumstances in internship may affect patient care.

The clinician's duty includes refraining from making self- serving emotional demands on the patient. Patients will express their suffering. It is the physician's duty to try to alleviate pain, not to tell the patient to keep quiet because the sound of his distress is annoying. Patients' outcries affect the emotional state and morale of the intern. If not managed adequately, tragic clinical situations may undermine his mood and judgment, which may eventually affect patient care. More immediately, the misery he encounters may increase the intern's emotional suffering and be transmitted to family members and others who are close to him.

Violence and trauma seen in the emergency room can be distressing, even to the experienced house officer. The harm that people inflict upon each other can be dreadful, unsettling even to one who has seen much of it. Wounds and injuries inflicted upon helpless victims, like children or bystanders caught in the crossfire of a drug gang war, can produce distress which may not be adequately processed internally under the pressure of treating those patients. For many residents and interns, an accumulation of such experiences can be emotionally burdensome. Many house officers protect themselves with the kind of hardening of spirit that may eventually lead to emotional isolation. In others it can lead to cynicism.

Coping With Horrors

Many interns cope with these horrifying experiences by suppressing them, trying to forget, concentrating on the medical and surgical aspects of the situation. Even those who are most able to suppress and forget are at times troubled by some of the events and horrors that they observed. These may continue to remain in the mind of the intern for hours, or longer. He may gain some relief by talking out those cases with a colleague at the end of the day, if that is possible. Others may gain some benefit by reviewing recent experiences in their own minds, silently at the end of the day. Of course, the end of the day may be 36 hours after the event, but many experiences have their impact for that length of time, or even longer.

One of the difficulties here, of course, is that by the end of the day, however long it may be, the intern is usually so tired that he finds it difficult to direct or to discipline his thoughts. He may think of nothing more than getting some rest or distraction. Still, it may be of some benefit to an intern to allow some time when his work is over, to see what floats to the surface of his mind, and to see whether any of the experiences may be recalled from his most recent duty hours. If he views such persistent recollections as a possibly emotionally stressful experience, he may allow himself to review and think through and feel through the reaction.

Emotional Debriefing

Many interns and residents have found that a systematic effort to review the experiences of the day can be beneficial. Generally, this means taking some time between leaving the hospital and arriving home to process his experience. This is often most comfortably done by talking with a colleague. Many can do it silently, alone. Walking home can provide the opportunity for such introspective emotional processing. If the intern's residence is nearby, it might be worth the effort to walk around the block a few times to provide the physical release and the emotional discharge that such thinking can provide. If one has a long commute, part of the time can be profitably spent in working through the emotionally trying events of the day. (see Table 2.1).

Such emotional processing can be personally protective for the intern. It can also serve to protect the intern's spouse or family.

Dealing with the stresses of the day can help the intern to refrain from inflicting the emotional effects on his family or whoever shares his home. It can reduce his irritability or despairing mood.

This is a process that need not be confined only to the intern. Senior residents and practicing physicians can make use of such end of the day emotional meditation. My home is about 40 miles away from my office, and for many years the time in driving home has provided an opportunity for me to sort through the problems of the day. I believe that this has enabled me to reduce my emotional demands on my family.

The variety of emotionally stressful events and circumstances that can arise in internship is extensive. Some of the most obvious are errors committed by the house officer: errors of commission or omission. Deaths of patients under one's care are dreadful but not totally avoidable despite enormous effort. Their emotional impact can be devastating if the intern has made an error that may have contributed to the patient's death. We direct intense efforts in our studies and practice to prevent such an occurrence, but those unfortunate errors may occur. It is essential that we prepare with every effort to prevent them, but also prepare to cope with such unhappy events, however rare they might be. (see Table 2.2).

One form of preparation is to imagine how one might feel after such an event. Would it be horror, regret, remorse, guilt? Will we be tempted to keep it secret, or would we prefer to tell someone, tell anyone? Will we want to be forgiven? One might think about how one's parents might feel if they knew about it. What will my mother think? What will my father think? My teachers? Will I try to hide it from myself? Will I try to place the blame on someone else, or something else? Will I ever be able to forgive myself for that kind of lethal mistake? Will I recognize that it is inevitable that such events occur? Will I try to learn from it to prevent making that mistake again? Will I try to teach it to others for the same purpose? Will I tell myself that it really doesn't matter because it's just another patient, and there are plenty of them, or will I tell myself that I must find some forgiveness and peace in order to go on to take care of other patients, and to take care of them successfully?

Emotionally Evocative Events

Emergency room duty is highly stressful with the imminence of death. Multiple emergencies like car accidents, bus accidents or fires, may overwhelm the emergency room staff. Some emergency situations are unfamiliar, especially to the beginning intern. These situations need to be anticipated, and in general ways at least, rehearsed mentally.

Regardless of its size and efficiency, any emergency unit can be overwhelmed with sufficient numbers of casualties. Most such facilities have prepared procedures for dealing with an overwhelming number of injured people. Usually the central feature of it is a triage system or a triage officer. This is someone who will sort the incoming patients into categories: those with treatable life threatening injuries, those with minor injuries and those whose injuries are probably beyond recovery. Treatment will be directed to those who are first to arrive and whose injuries are urgent. Some will die because of late arrival. Others may die or suffer irreparable damage as a consequence of the selection process.

From a rational point of view this is understandable, and is to be expected. From the point of view of the intern's emotional response, or the triage officer's emotional response, it may not be so easy to dismiss. This is especially true if the house officer is brought in contact with the families of those who have died or have been permanently impaired. Relatives' torment, anger and fears can overcome the physicians' barricade of detachment. This is one of the reasons why interns find the families of patients so threatening and why many house officers and other physicians try to avoid dealing with families.

Ordinarily, house officers are able to emphasize the cognitive aspect of such situations, reason it out, and accept the fact that not everyone can be treated adequately. But some experiences may penetrate the palisade of reason. One of the fatal outcomes may remind the house officer of someone in his personal life, a niece, a nephew, a cousin or brother. Another might be a reminder of his spouse or child.

The possibilities of errors in the rush of dealing with a large number of casualties is increased. Errors under such circumstances tend to be more readily adjusted to than in the quieter practice on an inpatient unit. Still, they can have a disturbing effect that may need to be examined explicitly.

Other stresses include threats to the person of the intern. This may be threats by violent patients, or through the transmission of lethal infections such as AIDS.

Response To Violence

Threats of violence and actual violent attacks are different, although one may merge into the other. Inner responses also need to be distinguished from external behavior in response to either the threat or the actuality. In terms of behavior, a threat of violence is usually best met with reasonable explanations and reassurance to the patient. At the same time, preparation for an actual attack should be instituted.

This primarily includes summoning help and preparing for avoidance by the intern. Actual attack by a patient should be responded to with avoidance or escape. At times, techniques of self defense may be necessary for the intern to extricate himself from the violent attack. Interns who are skilled in the techniques of any of the martial arts may be forced to apply what they know. It is essential, though, that an attack by a patient not be converted into a contest of physical prowess. The immediate urgent objective is self-preservation. Beyond that, the physician's responsibility continues to be not to harm, even to a patient who means harm to the physician. At times, self-defense requires inflicting harm upon one's attacker. It is not our duty as physicians to serve as targets for violence.

Affective Aftermath of Violence

The emotional response to such an event is something that requires preparation. If we can rehearse in advance how we might feel when confronted by a threat or by an actual attack, we may be able to explore the possibilities of terror, rage or helplessness. Emotional anticipation may help us to retain our cognitive control under such circumstances, and prevent us from sabotaging our own position in the event of an actual attack. The longer term emotional impact needs also to be explored. How would one feel after being attacked by a patient? How would such an experience affect future behavior with patients in general? How would it be affected if, in fact, one had been injured in such an attack?

The student may search his mind for models of violence. He may think back to past experiences with violence. Even violence that he has experienced in sports may be useful as a reference. He may have been involved in an accident, or even in close encounters with violence. To help himself to review and to anticipate, he may think back to experiences of violence experienced by relatives or friends. Certainly there is no shortage of violence depicted in television and movies, and he may use such fictional presentations to ask himself how he might react. One of the techniques that may be useful is comparing his expected reaction to a violent attack with that of characters that he sees in motion pictures or television stories.

Parallel to the threat of attack by a patient is the threat of exposure to HIV. The possibility of such exposure arises, for example, in handling a wound or performing surgery. The actuality of having been exposed to blood that is known to be infected by HIV is a separate though related phenomenon. Both of those circumstances need to be examined and rehearsed. Perhaps one of the most constructive outcomes of such anticipation would be adherence to appropriate precautions with respect to HIV exposure. One or two pairs of clean gloves in envelopes are even more basic equipment than the stethoscope.

Humiliation

A list of emotionally stressful events must include humiliating attacks by attending physicians or by angry senior residents. The most common consists of the senior person addressing the junior with the title, "Doctor", in a sarcastic tone.

Once again, the preparatory sequence consists of visualizing or otherwise imagining the event; examining the possible inner emotional responses; and then considering the various options with respect to action. Humiliating behavior by attending physicians or senior residents, inflicted upon junior residents, interns or students, has unfortunately probably been observed by most medical students, especially in the clinical years. If one has been the target of such abuse, one can re-examine it and reconsider how one might react and respond in the future. If one has been an observer of such behavior directed against classmates or others, one can review the responses as an observer, and the behaviors of those in attendance. One can then imagine one's self as the target for a future harassing event. Examination of the internal experience can provide some preparation for more effective external behavior.

In a subsequent chapter (#5), the corresponding sequence of expressive fantasies and rehearsal fantasies will be examined in more detail. These can provide immediate response and at least partial relief. The emotional decompression that expressive fantasies can offer increases the likelihood of a reasonable constructive response by the intern or student.

Recalling Mishaps And Disasters

Subsequent chapters of this book will examine a number of the stressful events that can be anticipated in internship, and adaptive tactics and strategies will be reviewed. In less time it takes to read these paragraphs, the student may imagine a number of fearsome circumstances. Examples include inability to accomplish a procedure such as tracheal intubation of an extensively burned fire-fighter or starting a blood transfusion in an obese pregnant patient with massive vaginal hemorrhage. The reader may also recall events that he or she has already observed in hospital situations. An intoxicated person might not report or even be aware of a fall and be in the early stages of a subdural hematoma that the intern does not suspect. A patient with gastrointestinal symptoms may have been suffering a myocardial infarction that the intern overlooks. A large number of severely burned people might be brought to the emergency room after a fire.

As they are remembered, the student can examine how he responded. One can also recall how others responded in those circumstances.

He can imagine how he might experience these events if he were in a position of responsibility as the intern. By scanning the spectrum of responses from incompetent panic and helplessness to efficiency and admirable leadership, the student can learn from what he has observed and can teach himself something about future responses.

As these events are recalled, one at a time, unpleasant emotions may arise. Ordinarily, such dysphoric reactions deter people from thinking about terrible events. Pressing one's own memory to confront them can have a deconditioning effect. With a reminder such as, "It isn't happening now. I'm merely recalling it," the feelings can be placed in perspective. Repeated mental exposure in this way can lead to an attenuation of feelings of horror, guilt, shame, or rage. The emotions will not reduce to zero nor is it apt to lead to undesirable callousness or insensitivity since the process of recall is under one's own direction (see Table 2.3).

The student can choose the person to whom he would most want to express these feelings as well as the most desirable time, place and method. He can choose the response that he would most want to receive: acceptance, forgiveness, soothing or commiseration.

He can repeat the dialogue mentally, with appropriate revisions until at least partial relief is attained. The process can be reinforced by discerning what could be learned from the stressful event. It can be mastered even further by finding what he could later teach to his juniors.

The duration of such an exercise is also under one's own control. It can be ended, in most instances, simply by willing it to end. Recall of particularly intense experiences may continue to reverberate, but can often be stopped by a distraction of some sort: thinking about something else, talking to someone or engaging in a pleasant or neutral activity.

Probably the most natural and constructive way to terminate such unpleasant recollections is first to direct one's thoughts to the specific circumstances that led to the pain-causing event: the patient's death or the humiliating error. Then one's thoughts can be directed to the actions in response. How might they have been done differently? What responses might have been more effective?

Then one's attention can be directed to the emotional reactions of the people involved in the event, including one's own. What were the immediate feelings of the participants? What were they later that day?

Having thought back to a past event that one observed, paying attention to currently aroused emotion, to emotion aroused at the time of the event and to responsive actions, attention can be directed forward to comparable events that might arise in the future. These can be played out mentally with improvements culled from the past. They can be replayed and revised until the best possible scenario is constructed. This can be committed to memory for later recall. Students may find it helpful to write a brief description of this mental vignette in a notebook or journal.

Then it can be set aside. After a while recall and rehearsal of another category of troublesome situations can be approached. Mental rehearsal is thus fortified by past observation. The next chapter will examine how past experience can be recruited to help one prepare in a more fundamental way for future stresses.

References

Barlow E: Rites of residency: New age stresses on the iron intern. Harvard Med Alumni Bull 1989;62(3):36-41.

Bayer R, Callahan D, Fletcher, et al.: The care of the terminally ill: Mortality and economics. N Engl J Med 1983;309:1490-1494.

Charach R, ed.: The Naked Physician: Poems about the Lives of patients and Doctors. Kingston, Ont., Quarry Press, 1990.

Cooke M, Sande MA: The HIV epidemic and training in internal medicine. N Engl J Med 1989;321:1334-1338.

Coste C: The risky business of becoming a doctor. New Physician 1978:27:28-31.

Doyle BB, Cline DW: Approaches to prevention in medical education, in The Impaired Physician. Scheiber SC, Doyle BB eds. New York, Plenum, 1983.

Dubin WR, Wilson SJ, Mercer C: Assaults against psychiatrists in outpatient settings. J Clin Psychiatry 1988;49:338-345.

Duffy JC: Emotional Issues in the Lives of Physicians. Springfield, IL, Charles C. Thomas, 1970.

Goldman JD: An elective seminar to teach first-year students the social and medical aspects of AIDS. J Med Educ 1987;62:557-561.

Hanh TN: The Miracle of Mindfulness: A Manual on Meditation. Revised edition, Boston, Beacon Press, 1987.

Landau C, Hall S, Waitman SA, et al: Stress in social and family relationships during medical residency. J Med Educ 1986;61:654-660.

Lion JR: Evaluation and Management of the Violent Patient. Springfield IL, Scharles C Thomas, 1972.

Marion R. The Intern Blues: The Private Ordeals of Three Young Doctors. New York, William Morrow and Co., Inc., 1989.

Mazie B: Job stress, psychological health and social supports of family practice residents. J Med Educ 1985;60:935-941.

McCall TB: The impact of long working hours on resident physicians. N Engl J Med 1988;318:775-778.

McCall TB: Sleep deprivation and performance of residents. JAMA 1989;261:859.

Messner E: Inspiration of psychotherapists by patients. Am J Psychiatry 1976;133:1462-1463.

Pawel BR: Sleep deprivation and resident performance. JAMA 1989;261:860.

Rosenberg DA, Silver HK: Medical student abuse: An unnecessary and preventable cause of stress. JAMA 1984;251:739-742.

Schowalter JE: Death and the pediatric house officer. Pediatrics 1970;75:706-710.

Sharaf M, Levinson D: The quest for omnipotence in professional training. Int J Psychiatry 1967;4:426-454.

Sheikh AA, ed: Imagery: Current Theory, Research, and Application. New York, Wiley, 1983.

Tardiff K, Maurice WL: The care of violent patients by psychiatrists. Can Psychiatric Assoc J 1977;22:83-86.

Thackery M: Therapeutics for Aggression. New York, Human Sciences Press, 1987.

Wachter RM: The impact of the acquired immunodeficiency syndrome on medical residency training. N Engl J Med 1986; 314:177-180.

Woolfolk RL, Lehrer PM, eds: Principles and Practice of Stress Management. New York, Guilford Press, 1984.

Table 2.1 →
Table 2.2 →
Table 2.3 →

TABLE 2.1 – Mental Debriefing of Distressing Events

A. *Identify the event through its effects:*
   1. Intrusive thoughts
   2. Interference with sleep
   3. Persistent and not easily dismissed
   4. Accompanied by anxiety
   5. Accompanied by anger, fear, guilt, sadness or other dysphoric emotions

B. *Identify:*
   1. Antecedents
   2. Consequences
   3. Ways that the event could be corrected, modified or improved
   4. What can be learned from the event
   5. What can be taught from the event

C. *Consider to whom you would want to describe the event:*
   1. What kind of response do you wish for?
      a. Acceptance
      b. Encouragement
      c. Forgiveness
      d. Respect
      e. Commiseration

   2. Could the person to whom you would want to describe it tolerate hearing it?

   3. Is that person available?

   4. Try talking it out with an internal dialogue.

   5. Decide whether to communicate interpersonally.

TABLE 2.2 – Sample List of Expectable Stresses

A. Errors affecting patients
    1. Commission or omission
    2. Outcomes: fatal, lasting, painful

B. Multiple simultaneous emergencies

C. Complications not caused by the intern
    1. By disease process
    2. By the patient himself

D. Death

E. AIDS

F. Violence

G. Sleep deprivation and fatigue

H. Incurable illness in patients

I. Less than optimal performance by the intern
    1. Procedures

    2. Cognitive activities: choice of treatment, diagnosis, recognition of complications

    3. Interpersonal relations with
        a. Patients
        b. Colleagues
        c. Teachers
        d. Patients' families

TABLE 2.3 – Planning to Surmount Expectable Stresses

A. Identify the stress

B. Visualize an example
   1. People, place, circumstances of that example

C. Imagine the consequences
   1. Thoughts
   2. Actions
   3. Feelings

D. Choose an ideal situation for expression of thoughts and feelings about the stress
   1. Person
   2. Place
   3. Method of expression

E. Choose a feasible situation for expression of thoughts and feelings
   1. Person
   2. Place
   3. Method

F. Identify a wished-for response
   1. Acceptance
   2. Forgiveness
   3. Soothing
   4. Commiseration

G. Rehearse expression of the feelings mentally
   1. Repeat and revise the expression until at least partial relief is attained

H. Identify what might be learned from this stress

I. Identify what might be taught to others about the stress

Chapter 3

Inventory Of Coping Strategies

Each of us has a repertoire of methods for dealing with life, ordinary events as well as stressful situations. Our habitual responses are so familiar that we may not even be consciously aware of them. For example, under stress some of us may work harder; read more; seek distractions, such as movies, or consolations like overeating. A kind of inertia seems to direct our ways of coping with life. Unless something directs us otherwise, we tend to follow the same patterns repeatedly. One of the advantages of looking explicitly at how we cope with stress is to allow us to select methods we judge to be adaptive, and perhaps reduce or discard those that are not. Reviewing past experience can bring coping strategies into conscious focus. Medical students have overcome challenges, acute and chronic. By examining these experiences, one can delineate how one tends to react.

Acute Stresses Recalled

For example, the reader can think back to his most intense, acute stress: an injury to self or sudden onset of illness; injury to a parent or someone else who is important. It may have been a natural disaster: flood, hurricane or perhaps a fire at home. Those events can come to mind more quickly than one can read these words. It may be a very unpleasant task to recall those events. For that I apologize, but the purpose is to learn from the experience and to apply it to forthcoming internship training.

Suppression Of Emotion

Many people attempt to cope with feelings by suppressing them. They despise feelings. They devalue them. They consider that emotions are for weaklings and should therefore be denied. In reviewing past experience with stress, one can examine whether such a method of coping was effective. Did it leave scars, or did it in fact, produce more vulnerability than it prevented? The question of suppression of emotion is usually not a matter of all or none.

People who somehow suppress virtually all emotion may find that they would serve their own purposes better if they allowed some feeling to emerge. In contrast, people who are overly emotional in situations of stress might benefit from an enhancement of neutralizing cognitive functioning. This can sometimes be accomplished through emphasis on rational behavior as one rehearses mentally.

At the time of those stressful events, what were the feelings; what where the thoughts; what was said; and what was done? Did the student get directly involved, or did he try to remove himself from the situation? Did he reach out to others for practical help or emotional help, or respond in a relatively isolated way? This process invites the reader to recall and, to some extent, reexperience intense moments. It is not my intention to demean those experiences by subjecting them to cold analysis. This effort is a part of professional preparation. We are trying to look at it with a sense of order and with thoroughness.

Learning from tragic events can help to neutralize some of the misery that they inflict. It can give additional meaning to lives that were lost or to pain that was suffered. If understanding them can contribute to personal growth, then a living memorial can be thus constructed from those experiences.

It might be useful to divide the experiences into time periods. One might review responses in the first few minutes of learning of the stressful event. What did the reader do or think in the next hour? Then what did he do in the remainder of the first twenty four hours?

Categories Of Responses

Stress will activate emotions, thoughts, wishes, impulses, bodily sensations, vocal communication, non-verbal communication and purposeful action. The reader could make a mental list, or even a written list, of the variety of responses recalled.

Emotions arise spontaneously. They can be suppressed, devalued or viewed as a signal of inner distress. Thoughts may be intentionally edited or amended. Wishes tend to be spontaneous, but may be suppressed, scorned or translated into actions designed to gratify or to defer. Whereas wishes are elective, needs are obligatory, but can be molded. Impulses, or intentions to act, can be suppressed, acceded to, or used as indicators of internal affect not consciously available. The value of delaying translation of an impulse into its corresponding action resides in the need for time to initiate mature cognitively based procedures. In deciding upon a course of action, it is essential to consider the alternatives and the consequences of each of them.

Bodily sensations such as aches, itches, heat, fullness, nausea or hunger can focus attention on an organ while distracting from its significance in terms of the whole person. Vocal communication – including expletives – is volitional and can be shaped and guided by judgment. Its significance as perceived by the auditor is not necessarily the same as that intended by the speaker.

Nonverbal communication, such as gesture, posture, facial expression or tone of voice, can inform others of one's inner state while the one remains oblivious. It often arises from preconscious or unconscious sources. In this way it may often be a more spontaneous and sincere communication, less subject to the deceptions and manipulations that can be introduced through verbal communication. Conscious observation of such communication in ourselves as well as in others can influence personal effectiveness. Action can be based on reason, optimism, confidence, and determination or can be heavily influenced by unassimilated dread.

The foregoing is a brief and far from complete list of responses. It may serve as a table of categories that the reader can enrich or modify in accordance with his own experience. (see Table 3.1).

We can look back at stressful events and find that the pain caused by them may be alleviated to some extent by satisfaction we may feel about our own responses to them. We may have contributed something constructive to the situation. It is possible, also, that the dreadful situation may have become even more painful because of regret or self-blame resulting from dissatisfaction with some of what we thought or did. Many people have had second thoughts and have felt remorse about their performances under stress. A common thought is, "If I had it to do over again, I would do it differently."

Improving The Repertoire

Learning from such experiences in ways that can be applied constructively in the future can sometimes reduce the sting. Situations rarely recur exactly, but analytic hindsight can lead to useful foresight. We can winnow the better procedures from the worse. If we judge them to be ineffective or destructive, even some of our spontaneous responses can be limited, curtailed, or even suppressed. Others can be learned and added to the repertoire.

A student offered encouragement, consolation, and concern for others. He felt discouraged that his friends and colleagues did not reciprocate. Eventually he felt deprived and depleted. With some professional assistance, he learned to recognize his own wishes for empathy from others. He was able, with some rehearsal, to communicate those desires appropriately. Subsequently he received gratifying responses in meaningful ways, and he continued his generous former conduct as well.

This person employed the golden rule as a substitute for awareness of his own needs as well as for its own intrinsic value. He was able to add awareness of his own natural wishes for responsiveness from others and an ability to communicate them appropriately.

Responses To Chronic Stresses

It is useful, also, to make an inventory of responses to chronic stresses. Internship will present the young physician with numerous stresses that continue over an extended period. Residency training itself continues for three to eight years, depending upon one's specialty. The great demands of time, the discipline and the restricted income can contribute substantially to the resident's problems. Some of these will be examined in detail in future chapters.

As with the acute stresses, the student can benefit by thinking back on his own life history. Chronic stresses will come to mind very promptly. They may consist of long periods of illness in one's self, in parents or close relatives. The ravages of poverty or bigotry may be all too familiar to some students. Recalling such circumstances may also be painful and distressing. Once again, I am sorry to evoke such emotions. I hope that their re-examination will lead to constructive learning.

In a seminar, a student recalled taking care of her mother following a stroke. She shared the work with her sister and brother but immersed herself in her studies. Her sister and brother spent much time together and developed a closeness that she has never been able to share fully. Looking back, she wished she had coped with those sad and draining years with more intimacy. She intended to respond to future stresses with more contact and connection with the important people in her life.

Changes With Time

Reviewing one's responses to long-term stresses can be accomplished in a manner similar to the review of the acute situations. In this case, the time periods, of course, tend to be much longer: days, weeks, months, sometimes even years. Over such extended periods we may find a variety of adaptive mechanisms. In fact, we may see that we have started with one approach, like avoidance, and replaced it with intense involvement. These changes may have been functions of changes in the situation or modifications that came about with personal maturation. Our objective is to sort out what worked constructively from what did not and to devise ways to retain the better and relinquish the worse.

One of the measures of effective response is the preservation of a reasonable degree of self-esteem. This important internal attitude can be diminished by inwardly directed anger. This is apparent in a person who feels, "I hate myself". Less obvious inwardly aimed attacks masquerade as judgments of worth or quality. Examples are: feelings of being stupid, inadequate, fat, ugly, cowardly, lazy, or weak. Such vitriol would readily be seen as hostile if expressed towards another person. Opprobrium could hardly be considered a helpful or corrective observation.

Self esteem can also be undermined by various forms of self-punishment. Examples are smoking, excessive drinking, neglect of rest and recreation, avoidance of friends and provoking arguments with spouse or lover. Any source of dysphoria or misery over which one has meaningful influence can be considered a possible instance of personally imposed penance.

A feeling of worth is built upon internalized images of parents and others as they were perceived to respond to the individual, especially during infancy and childhood. The requirements, desires and expectations of these influential people affect the sense of personal value and satisfaction. Superimposed upon these expectations are the standards that the individual develops later in relatively independent ways.

A student whose father had spent years in a prisoner of war camp grew to admire fortitude and perseverance. He experienced privations and burdensome work as challenges. He viewed them as exercises that would make him stronger.

The process of inventory need not be confined to one's own responses. We can study the coping mechanisms employed by others. How did relatives or other people deal with the situation in which we found ourselves? How did friends deal with that same situation if they were involved, or with comparable situations in their own lives? In making this relatively objective review of adaptive methods and styles we can examine not only our own history and those of our friends and relatives, we can extend it to people that we have heard about or read about. We can even contemplate the adaptive mechanisms of fictional characters. (see Table 3.2).

The student may be acquainted with representations of physicians in printed literature, motion pictures or television. Some are absurd and simplistic, particularly in many television versions, but some are realistic and even admirable. Fictional characters in other occupations may also serve as models.

Romantic or dramatic representations can be inspiring. A character like Arrowsmith can serve as a model in an era in which medical idealism is in short supply.

Live Models

Ready at hand, of course, are the actual residents, attending physicians, teachers and professors, who provide examples of desirable adaptive styles as well as styles that may be repugnant or destructive. To varying degrees, students will observe such examples spontaneously. Often the reactions are largely emotional and random. The student may benefit from observing systematically. (see Table 3.3).

A resident or other teacher need not be a totally admirable person to serve as a source for a specific adaptive method. Even instructors and others who may be unappealing in many ways may still demonstrate one or more coping procedures that are effective, ethical and relevant. These can be learned just as one learns technics for palpating an acute abdomen or for visualizing the retina from clinicians whom one may not idolize personally.

A student described one of her instructors as disgustingly absorbed with, and boastful about his luxurious possessions and expensive style of living. Yet she admired him for his meticulous clinical work and his unstinting availability when complications or emergencies arose. Another attending was described as aloof and distant in professional situations, but was found to be warm and devoted to her family and to students who actively sought her guidance or counsel.

It is valuable to try to anticipate which of the adaptive mechanisms will be feasible in internship and in succeeding years of residency. It is also useful to sort out which of these coping strategies can be practiced currently during the remaining time in medical school. Examples of specific methods are listed in Table 3.4.

Preparing an inventory of effective adaptive methods is part of a larger effort to marshal favorable factors to benefit the future intern. This larger effort includes an accumulation of personal resources and skills to be discussed in the chapters ahead.

References

Dimsdale JE: Stress during the internship year. in, Coombs RH, May DS, Small GW eds: Inside Doctoring: Stages and Outcomes in the Professional Development of Physicians. New York, Praeger, 1986.

Earle M: Physician Heal Thyself! Minneapolis, MN, Comp Care Publishers, 1989.

Figley CR, ed: Trauma and Its Wake. New York, Brunner Mazel, 1985.

Gaensbauer TJ, Mizner GL: Developmental stresses in medical education. Psychiatry 1980;43:60-70.

Herzog DB, Wysak G, Stern TA: Patient-generated dysphoria in house officers. J Med Educ 1984;59:869-874.

Keller KL, Koenig WJ: Management of stress and prevention of burnout in emergency physicians. Ann Emerg Med 1989;18:42-47.

Kelly JA, Bradlyn AS, Dubbert, et al: Stress management training in medical school. J Med Educ 1982;57:91-99.

Messner E, Groves JE, Schwartz JH, eds: Autognosis: How Psychiatrists Analyze Themselves. Chicago, Year Book Medical Publishers, 1989.

Myers MF: Marital distress among resident physicians. Can Med Assoc J 1986;134:117-118.

Myers MF: Doctors' Marriages: A Look at the Problems and Their Solutions. New York, Plenum, 1988.

Nelson FG, Henry WF: Psychosocial factors seen as problems by family practice residents and their spouses. J Fam Prac 1978; 6:581-589.

Pepitone-Arreola-Rockwell F, Rockwell D, Core N: Fifty-two medical student suicides. Am J Psychiatry 1981;138:198-201.

Pfifferling JH, Blum JC, Wood W: The prevention of physician impairment. J Fla Med Assoc 1981;68:268-273.

Quill TE, Williamson PR: Healthy approaches to physician stress. Arch Intern Med 1990;150:1857-1861.

Rich CL, Pitts FN: Suicide by male physicians during a five year period. Am J Psychiatry 1976;136:1089-1090.

Ritchie K: Sleep deprivation and performance of residents. JAMA 1989;261:859-860.

Rosenberg DA, Silver HK: Medical student abuse: An unnecessary and preventable cause of stress. JAMA 1984;251:739-742.

Rotbart HA, Nelson WL, Krantz J, et al: The developmental process of residency education. Issues of stress and happiness. Am J Dis Child 1985;1349:762-765.

Schowalter JE: Death and the pediatric house officer. Pediatrics 1970;75:706-710.

Shapiro E, Lowenstein L, eds: Becoming a Physician: Development of Values and Attitudes in Medicine. Cambridge, MA, Allinger, 1979.

Sharaf M, Levinson D: The quest for omnipotence in professional training. Int J Psychiatry 1967;4:426-454.

Siegel B, Donnelly JC: Enriching personal and professional development: The experience of a support group for interns. J Med Educ 1978;53:908-914.

Silver RL, Wortzman CB: Coping with undesirable life events. In: Garber J, Seligman MEP, eds: Human Helplessness. New York, Academic Press 1980:279-340.

Stein HF: The Psychodynamics of Medical Practice. Berkeley, University of California Press, 1985.

Vaillant GE, Sobowale NC, McArthur C: Some psychologic vulnerabilities of physicians. N Engl J Med 1972;287:372-375.

Woolfolk RL, Lehrer PM, eds: Principles and Practice of Stress Management. New York, Guilford Press, 1984.

TABLE 3.1 – Coping Methods and Homeostasis

- Coping mechanisms or methods help to maintain homeostasis in various personality functions
  - Emotions
  - Thoughts
  - Wishes
  - Impulses
  - Bodily sensations
  - Vocal communication
  - Action
  - Non-verbal communication

TABLE 3.2 – Evaluation of Effectiveness of Coping Methods

- Ability to manage the stressful situation
- Relief of pain and distress in:
  - Self
  - Significant others
  - Distant others
- Consequences regarding duties, education, work or capacity to teach
- Effects on personal development
- Self-esteem and self-respect
- What was learned
- What can be taught

TABLE 3.3 – Sources of Inventory of Coping Methods

- Personal history
- Experience of family
- Experience of friends
- Live models
- Historical or biographical figures
- Fictional characters

Table 3.4 – **Examples of Coping Methods**

- Using experience
- Trying to find humor
- Engaging in distractions
- Taking action
- Exercising
- Making plans
- Using expletives

Chapter 4

Thought, Emotion And Inner Dialogue

An internal diagnostic measure found useful by many people is the balance between thought and emotion. The myriad tasks an intern must perform may interfere with clear awareness of his inner state. Conscious volitional observations of the inner condition may help. A simple procedure is to ask, fairly often, "How do I feel now?" As people mature, they develop a sense of an appropriate intensity of emotion for each of various circumstances. These are subjective responses and may differ widely among individuals.

What feelings might a student expect when the senior resident confirms his diagnosis? How might it differ from confirmation by an autopsy report? What might be felt in seeing a patient's cardiac function restored after a code? What are the feelings in response to cardiac arrest during surgery?

In the personal realm what are the subjective responses to seeing one's father or mother after a long absence? How does it differ if that parent is in a cheerful mood or a gloomy state?

A student reported that she rushed home after she was informed that her mother had suffered a stroke. She saw her mother with her face paralyzed on one side, and unable to speak. Her right arm and leg were immobile. The student said she felt nothing, no emotion. After about a half hour, she began to feel an eeriness that she was experiencing no sadness, shock, or other recognizable emotion.

Another student cried when he saw motion pictures in which fathers showed tenderness or protectiveness to sons. This student had not cried after his own fathers' death.

Under conditions of stress, some do not notice their emotional state until it reaches a painful level. This may be manifested by unruffled competence at work followed by irritability or explosive anger at home at the end of the day. Another pattern may be despair and tearfulness on weekends or other times free of duties. Some people do not notice their emotional depletion until other people call it to their attention.

"You seem worn out".

"I haven't heard you laugh in weeks."

Developing A Baseline

Cultivation of self-awareness and development of a baseline for emotional intensity can enable the student or intern to recognize excessive intensities of emotion or unexpected blandness. If a student flies into a rage when a pen fails to write, or when his toast has been scorched, he can probably recognize that his degree of irritability is somewhat higher than his usual. If he becomes outraged when his instructor respectfully disagrees with a diagnosis, the intensity of anger is probably over baseline. Similarly, students may experience other feelings, like sadness, envy or despair in circumstances that do not warrant such strong reactions as measured against that student's own usual responses.

Emotional Proprioception

We human beings have a kind of emotional proprioceptive sense akin to the neurological sense of position. The reader can instantly become aware of the location and orientation of left foot or right index finger. Prior to reading those words, he was probably not conscious of them. In a similar way, a person can become aware of the quality and intensity of feeling that he may be experiencing at any moment. By thinking of it consciously the reader may become aware of a reaction to the material on this page. In academic or clinical situations, the student can become aware of his emotional state and what he considers the degree of appropriateness of his feelings. By taking samples of the inner milieu from time to time, the student can calibrate his emotional system. Deviations can serve as a signal that something unusual is happening, and that perhaps the subjective response is inconsistent with what he generally experiences.

A major goal in this kind of self-observation is recognition of internal changes before they go too far. Intensity of emotion can be insufficient as well as excessive. If some one close to us is injured and we feel nothing, the affective system is deviating from its usual function, in most people. Some people are characteristically arid emotionally, often automatically substituting thoughts in the place of feelings.

A physician reported that her husband was irresponsible, undependable, and offered almost no help in child care or household chores. When asked how she felt about it, she presented examples, events and remembered conversations. When invited gently to say what she had felt at the time, she presented more facts and events. When encouraged to say how she felt when recalling those events, she described more examples. Her attention was called to the absence of inner states like sadness, disappointments, or annoyance. She was surprised, but said that in relation to her husband, she could "feel" only that his behavior was unfair.

Floods of Thoughts

Comparable observations and subjective measurements of intensity of thought can also be cultivated. Medical students are accustomed to a profusion of thought, and so are interns and residents. Intensity of thought may exceed what is familiar. Thoughts may seem to take on a life of their own, and may recur in an unproductive repetition. Consciousness may be flooded with them, preventing the student or intern from falling asleep even when there is time for sleep. Recognition that thoughts have become unduly intense can serve as a signal that something is amiss.

Altered Equilibrium

Some people have a tendency to react to stress with an excess of feeling; others with an excess of cognition. Still others experience combinations of excesses of both. Most students function with a balance of emotion and thought in their day to day experience. It is often helpful to recognize the development of unexpected imbalances that may arise in response to stressful circumstances. A student who is accustomed to a preponderance of cognitive internal activity may be alerted when he recognizes an unexpected preponderance of affect. Such observations can alert the student to a disturbance of this dynamic equilibrium.

An intern who had considered himself fairly tough-minded, unexpectedly wept at the death of a neonate. This was the first time he had cried about an event at the hospital in more than 7 months. A single episode of tearfulness is not an indication of emotional instability. In fact it may represent a restoration of balance. It may

46

exemplify maturational progress which might lead to improved ability to respond with appropriate emotionality to human tragedy. If the formerly dry-eyed intern begins to cry frequently, especially without clear provocation, a disequilibrium may be developing.

Activation Of Inner Dialogue

Once the altered balance has been sensed, an inner dialogue can be activated. This is a device that has been reported useful by many. It serves to make the inner state more explicit. The resident can ask, "What's going on in here?" The answer might be, "My thoughts seem to be running free". Or, "My anger is getting out of hand".

The inner dialogue can be pushed forward with the goal of understanding the current situation better, adding perspective and discovering effective ways of responding. For example, if thoughts seem to be predominant, the resident can search for the corresponding feelings. If he is flooded with emotions, a search for the associated thoughts and participating events can be pursued.

In either case, one can question one's self about what may be the specific provocation of this reaction, of this imbalance of affect and cognition. The most common and obvious review would be directed toward the current situation or personal interaction. Going beyond, the resident can ask, "Am I reacting to something in the past?" This brings to bear a review of recent events and reactions.

He can ask, "Why am I feeling this so strongly?"
"Have I felt this way in the past?"
"Under what circumstances?"
"With whom?"

When the resident's consciousness is flooded with thoughts, and feelings are not available, or when the intensity of feeling is diminished or apparently absent, other questions can be raised.

"Is there a feeling that I am avoiding?"
"Is this a symptom of exhaustion?"

Residents can usually recognize such emotions as annoyance or sympathy, sadness or joy. When commonly experienced feelings are absent or markedly attenuated, we may search for substitutes. Sometimes emotions are represented by images or fantasies. Allowing one's self to be aware of these fantasies can suggest the quality of emotion that is latent. For example, an image of someone in a rage or an image of someone crying or laughing can suggest that those feelings would be experienced except that something is blocking them. Another substitute function may be impulses. The student may not be aware of emotions or fantasies but may have an urge to do something: to act, to leave the room, to punch someone, to lie down and cry. The student may not act on those impulses but may still be aware of their presence and of the temptation to carry them into action. These also can serve as clues to the nature of the missing feelings. (see Table 4.1 and 4.2).

Some experience their emotions as physical sensations. These may be a lump in the throat, prickling sensation in the back of the neck, a heaviness in the abdomen, pressure behind the eyes, or any of numerous physical sensations. One of the keys to translating these sensations into recognizable affects is to ask one's self, "What were the circumstances under which these sensations appeared in the past?" Such patterns can be enlightening and useful.

The first occurrence of a symptom tends to be especially informative. This holds true for psychosomatic or emotionally activated symptoms just as it applies to the symptoms of purely medical or surgical disorders.

A young physician reported that he had suffered lower back pain that arose after he held his own infant son. A resident reported experiencing persisting stiffness in his shoulder that he first felt after serving as a pall bearer for a friend who had died of AIDS. Others have described nausea that they had previously felt following the deaths of relatives. Many have described feeling nauseated by scenes of death or of funerals that they had seen in motion pictures or television plays. (see Table 4.3).

Activation of the internal dialogue can, itself, be a restabilizing procedure. It may serve to neutralize a feeling of aloneness that often complicates difficult situations. Some students may find that one or another of the imagined speakers resembles people in the student's life. One of the voices may represent a parent, mentor, good friend, older brother or sister, someone who provides nurturance, guidance, encouragement, or soothing. The appearance of such comforting people in the inner dialogue may be spontaneous or it can be cultivated. This adaptive technique can be highly effective and widely applicable.

References

Cassell EJ: Talking with Patients: Volume 1. The Theory of Doctor-patient Communication. Cambridge, Mass, MIT Press, 1985.

Cassell EJ: Talking with Patients: Volume 2. Clinical Technique. Cambridge, Mass, MIT Press, 1985.

Chappel JN, Schnoll SH: Physician attitudes: Effect on the treatment of chemically dependent patients. JAMA 1977;237:2318-2319.

Dubovsky SL, Schrier RW: The mystique of medical training: Is teaching perfection in medical house-staff training a reasonable goal or a precursor of low self esteem? JAMA 1983;250:3057-3058.

Earle M: Physician Health Thyself! Minneapolis, MN, Comp Care Publishers, 1989.

Glick SM: Humanistic medicine in a modern age. N Engl J Med 1982;304:1036-1038.

Gottschalk LA: How to Do Self-Analysis and Other Self Psycho-therapies, Northvale, NJ, Jason Aronson, 1989.

Hanh TN: The Miracle of Mindfulness: A Manual on Meditation. Revised edition, Boston, Beacon Press, 1987.

Horowitz MI: Image Formation and Psychotherapy. New York, Jason Aronson, 1983.

Link RN, Feingold AR, Charap MH, et al: Concerns of medical and pediatric house officers about acquiring AIDS from their patients. Am J Public Health 1988;78:455-459.

Messner E: Autognosis: Diagnosis by the use of the self, in Lazare A ed: Outpatient Psychiatry. Baltimore, Williams and Wilkins Co. 1979.

Morris PE, Hampson PJ: Imagery and Consciousness. New York, Academic Press, 1983.

Rosenberg DA, Silver HK: Medical student abuse: An unnecessary and preventable cause of stress. JAMA 1984;251:739-742.

Schowalter JE: Death and the pediatric house officer. Pediatrics 1970;75:706-710.

Sheikh AA, ed: Imagery: Current Theory, Research and Application. New York, Wiley, 1983.

Singer JL: Imagery and Day Dreaming Methods in Psychotherapy and Behavior Modification. New York, Academic Press, 1984.

Smith RC: Teaching interviewing skills to medical students: The issue of "countertransference." J Med Educ 1984;59:582-588.

Woolfolk RL, Lehrer PM, eds: Principles and Practice of Stress Management. New York, Guilford Press, 1984.

Zinn WM: Doctors have feelings too. JAMA 1988;259:3296-3298.

Table 4.1 →
Table 4.2 →
Table 4.3 →

TABLE 4.1 — Management of Cognitive-Affective Imbalance

Activate an inner dialogue

Cast the speakers' roles
  — Two parts of one's own self
  — If the emotions are too intense, cast the emotional subjective part of the self, and a calm, reflective, mature, objective friend, parent, sibling, teacher, coach or mentor

  — Allow the calm other voice to ask cognitive questions such as: "What do you think?" or "What are the facts?"

  — If the thoughts are too intense, intrusive or obsessional, cast the cognitive part of the self and an earthy, feeling emotive friend, parent, sibling, et al

  — Allow the emotive other voice to ask affective questions such as, "What do you feel?" or "How might that feel to someone else?"

Always be sure that at least one voice in the dialogue is friendly, supportive, comforting — on your side

Examine alternatives to emotions such as fantasies, impulses or bodily sensations

TABLE 4.2 – Alternatives to Direct Emotion

- Fantasies
- Impulses
- Physical Sensations
- Nonverbal expressions
  - Tone of voice
  - Facial expression
  - Posture
  - Spontaneous actions

TABLE 4.3 – Goals in Management of Cognitive-Affective Imbalance

- Intense emotions become understandable
  - They subside to expectable intensity
  - They become less painful
- Intrusive thoughts subside to expectable intensity and associated emotions emerge
- Inner turmoil and dysphoria diminish

Chapter 5

Constructive Uses of Directed Fantasies

Imagination is a familiar yet wonderful feature of human experience. Consideration of it is intended to suggest adaptive applications for the intern. Fantasy is used here to denote imaginings of any variety.

Adaptive Use of Imagination

Imagination is most commonly useful in planning. Mental visualization can help in preparing for a task. We may imagine ourselves about to examine a patient, or to carry out a procedure, or picturing the road that we are going to follow in driving home. Sounds, textures or thoughts may also enter awareness in planning. These processes are so familiar we often do not notice them.

In ordinary experience, imagination will serve its function and then recede into the background. In that way, it is similar to muscles, limbs or other body parts. We become aware of them sometimes when they are in use. We may also become aware of them when they are needed and are, for some reason, not able to function satisfactorily. Typically, imaginings will arise spontaneously in circumstances in which they can assist in accomplishing a task. We are also able to direct the process of imagination in a conscious and volitional mode.

Directed fantasies can be highly useful in adapting to, or coping with, emotionally stressful situations. They can be divided into two main categories: the expressive fantasy, and the rehearsal fantasy.

Expressive Fantasies

An expressive fantasy enables one to discharge feelings in circumstances that do not permit vocalization. They can be particularly helpful if an instructor is berating and humiliating a student in the presence of some of his classmates. The student may not feel free, or the circumstances may not permit him to respond with the hostility or sarcasm that the abuser provokes. He can, however, express it to himself silently in a directed fantasy. The victim can imagine himself saying what he would want to say or can imagine doing something to make the harasser uncomfortable. He can picture other people jeering or attacking the instructor verbally. Some people an actually feel relief as anger is discharged in this intrapsychic process. Others can achieve that sort of relief with practice. Employment of these fantasies need not prevent – and, in fact, may facilitate – academic learning. That assumes that the abusive instructor has something to teach medically.

Fantasy Distinct From Action

Essential in all considerations of directed fantasy is that the distinction be maintained between imagining something and the corresponding action. The privacy of one's mind can be a refuge. Even non-verbal communications need be suppressed at times. Life is such that sometimes expression of emotion by the student or intern may make things worse. In some circumstances, such as dealing with a violent or potentially violent patient, external expression of hostility can be dangerous.

Hostile or provocative behavior by clinicians appears to increase the frequency or severity of physical attacks by patients, according to surveys. Internal management of rage or fear by the clinician can help lead to calm and rational outward demeanor. Reassuring and soothing words and manner appear to be relatively effective in calming irrational patients.

Directed fantasies can be brought to bear in real time, at the moment when the emotionally charged situation is actually occurring. They can also be used following the incident. One can review the experience repeatedly, searching for ways to discharge the feeling that one has had to contain. Picturing oneself responding fully and freely to a tormenting superior or a threatening patient can be relieving and can even be pleasurable. Repetition exactly or with variations can serve to release increments of feeling. In psychiatry, working through is the designation given such a process of gradual decompression and assimilation.

Some people are diffident about even imagining themselves in a confrontive situation. One very cautious and well mannered student was talking about an attending physician whose sarcasm and biting jokes embarrassed many of the residents. The student imagined that the department head walked in at a time when the attending physician was abusing the house officers. He imagined the department head reprimanding and then firing the doctor right there. Then he hesitated, and said, "No, that's too severe—he shouldn't be fired". He reminded himself that this was only a fantasy and that he could be freer in the retribution. He then allowed himself to think of the physician being fired, expelled from the medical society, publicly exposed as a bad example, having his statements corrected by an expert, and exposed as a charlatan.

Another student described a patient who was crude and threatening to the members of the hospital staff. She pictured that patient being beaten up by thugs who were hired for the purpose.

For many people, the effectiveness of a directed fantasy lies in imagining a scene that is not only affect laden, but intense. Sometimes the more uncivilized the fantasy, the more effective it can be in the management of pent-up emotion. Instead of telling the instructor in one's fantasy that he is a self-centered egotistical bigot, it might be just that much more enjoyable to picture hitting him in the face with a cream pie. Whereas one might conceivably reply angrily to a superior, it is extremely unlikely that the cream pie or other weapon will be at hand, or that it would be used. The more unrealistic, the easier it is to maintain the distinction between the fantasy and its corresponding enactment.

It may be necessary to intensify the violence of an expressive fantasy in order to discharge the anger that was generated. For example, the cream pie may not be a sufficiently punishing weapon. The student might think of using rotten eggs or over-ripe tomatoes as attack weapons, or, in fact, might even think in terms of violent and injurious weapons such as a club or other instrument. As long as the distinction between fantasy and action is clearly maintained, there is no hazard in permitting the violence to accelerate in one's imagination.

Rehearsal Fantasies

Rehearsal fantasies are mental practices for situations that might eventually be converted into action. If one has been hurt or disappointed by a friend and wants to talk about it, a useful, perhaps even necessary, prerequisite is for the overly intense emotions to be worked through first. The expressive fantasies need to be employed fully until the pain or resentment have subsided to a comfortable level. At that point, the student can practice what to say and how to say it.

It is often desirable to imagine the conversation in some detail with a number of verbal interchanges. One can imagine what one wants to say and then imagine the other person's possible responses. This can lead to further conversation in the mind, with the possibility of revision. One can try different scenarios, until one finds one that is satisfactory and is likely to produce something constructive. Such rehearsal fantasies can be used in anticipation of difficult conversations with virtually anyone: spouse, relatives, colleagues, or others.

One of the objections that is sometimes raised about the use of rehearsal fantasies is that it diminishes the spontaneity of one's behavior. It can, but sometimes unrestricted affective responses can be less than desirable. In the exhausted and irritable state that is common to interns, they may blurt words to their spouses, lovers or children that they may later regret. They may become explosively angry or sarcastic and thereby hurt people whom they profoundly cherish. The procedure suggested here is a selective and focussed restriction of spontaneity. It need not stifle an otherwise free spirit.

Performance Fantasies

A major subset of rehearsal fantasies includes the performance fantasies. These are images that can be employed to practice physically demanding procedures requiring skill and coordination. Obvious examples are surgical technics, catheterizations, endotracheal intubations, or any of the delicate manipulations required by endoscopy. These fantasies are useful in perfecting the movements necessary for carrying out such medical and surgical procedures. They are akin to the imagery employed by athletes to perfect a tennis stroke, a running stride, a dive or any other activity in sports by picturing their own performance. They include imagining touch and proprioceptive sensations in addition to visualizing one's self carrying out the procedure.

These images can add greatly to the actual experience of the procedures. They can take the place of many repetitions. In order to imagine the physical sensations as well as the visual process of a procedure, the intern must first have experienced the activity. After he has performed it a number of times and has received instruction, or has been observed, or has observed himself, he can then imagine carrying out the procedure with increasing skill to the point of near perfection.

The range of applicability of performance imaging can include the poise that is desirable in a clinical presentation, in grand rounds or in presenting a lecture. It can be used for the direct hands-on procedures of the physical examination and need not be limited to the highly technical use of modern medical equipment. (see Table 5.1).

The expressive and rehearsal fantasies described above may seem familiar to some readers. These are mental capabilities that many people evolve in the process of maturing. Many students and residents have reported that by practicing directed fantasies they have become more skillful in their use. Consequently these fantasies have become more effective for them: more powerful in helping them to manage emotionally difficult situations and in working out conflicted and sometimes painful, personal relationships.

References

Gottschalk LA: How to Do Self-Analysis and Other Self Psychotherapies, Northvale, NJ, Jason Aronson, 1989.

Hanh TN: The Miracle of Mindfulness: A Manual on Meditation. Revised edition, Boston, Beacon Press, 1987.

Horowitz MI: Image Formation and Psychotherapy. New York, Jason Aronson, 1983.

Messner E: Autognosis: Diagnosis by the use of the self, in Lazare A ed: Outpatient Psychiatry. Baltimore, Williams and Wilkins Co. 1979.

Messner E, Groves JE, Schwartz JH, eds: Autognosis: How Psychiatrists Analyze Themselves. Chicago, Year Book Medical Publishers, 1989.

Morris PE, Hampson PJ: Imagery and Consciousness. New York, Academic Press, 1983.

Myers MF: Marital distress among resident physicians. Can Med Assoc J 1986;134:1117-1118.

Myers MF: Doctors' Marriages: A Look at the Problems and Their Solutions. New York, Plenum, 1988.

Pennebaker JW, Susman JR: Disclosure of traumas and psychosomatic processes. Soc Sci Med 1988;26:327-322.

Sheikh AA ed: Imagery: Current Theory, Research, and Application. New York, Wiley, 1983.

Singer JL: Imagery and Day Dreaming Methods in Psychotherapy and Behavior Modification. New York, Academic Press, 1984.

Smith RC: Teaching interviewing skills to medical students: The issue of "countertransference." J Med Educ 1984;59:582-588.

Woolfolk RL, Lehrer PM, eds: Principles and Practice of Stress Management. New York, Guilford Press, 1984.

Yager J: Teaching Guided Imagery. Academic Psychiatry 1989; 13:31-38.

TABLE 5.1 – Directed Fantasies

- An expressive fantasy permits a form of release or discharge of emotion

- A rehearsal fantasy serves to prepare for an action or for an actual event

- Both types of fantasy are distinct from corresponding actions. They are mental, internal, and not outwardly perceived.

- An impulse is a fantasy combined with an urge to act. It, too, is distinct from the corresponding action. An impulse can be contained and remain mental and internal.

- Performance fantasies can supplement practice to enhance skill, poise and precision.

Chapter 6

Advantages of Physical Release

The expressive fantasies described earlier were distinguished from their corresponding actions. The usefulness of the fantasies is, in part, related to their capacity to be employed during social or clinical situations. They take place silently within the mind of the student or intern and thus are immediately available under virtually any circumstances. However, most people also require outward (i.e., physical) expression of emotions or attitudes. Under appropriate circumstances, such expression of feelings can be gratifying, relieving and constructive.

Talking about intense experiences is often helpful. At times, however, feelings of frustration or anger may become so intense that ordinary conversation, even with intimate friends or relatives, may be insufficient. For those circumstances, it is sometimes a relief to write, doodle or draw pictures, but more often it is necessary to perform some sort of gross muscular action.

Gross Motor Expressiveness

Some people derive release from athletics: running, tennis, handball, basketball, or swimming. Such activities may not be readily available to the intern, and they may be too time consuming. For a person with even minimal skill at tennis, pounding a ball against a backboard can be gratifying at times of frustration or resentment. In some cases it can be enhanced by imagining an offensive person's face on the ball. This exemplifies enhancement of vigorous action with a directed fantasy.

A physical expression of rage or frustration that is readily available is pounding a broom against a mattress. This is safe, relatively quiet, and permits expression of emotion for as long as necessary — or until the broom handle breaks.

For people who require vocal expression of feeling, shouting into a bed pillow can serve as a release. The procedure consists of folding the pillow double, taking a deep breath, pressing it against one's face, and shouting as loud and as long as one needs. This can provide considerable release without disturbing neighbors or others in the same dwelling. To some readers, these devices may seem a bit primitive, but they are appropriate to the feral affects aroused under some of the stressful situations of internship.

Rage is not the only feeling that is aroused in internship. Sadness, horror, humiliation, despair, terror and other painful emotions may be aroused to an intensity that demands release. Crying is appropriate for men as well as for women. For these feelings, also, the joy of motion and muscular activity may serve as a comfort and a release.

Limitation of Athletic Opportunities

Sleep deprivation, fatigue and limitation of free time will severely reduce the intern's freedom to engage in athletics. This may be particularly distressing and frustrating to medical students and interns who are athletes accustomed to a great deal of physical activity. Their skills are apt to diminish, even though their talent remains, with the reduction of opportunity for practicing their sports. A highly trained, accomplished athlete will experience additional frustration observing his performance deteriorate during house officer training. This is a phenomenon that needs be thought through in advance. If the athletic medical student looks ahead and expects it, then he will be in a better position to cope with such decline.

Many athletic residents, for this reason, decide to give up their primary sport entirely rather than to perform at less than their usual excellent level. This is a decision that needs to be made by each individual. At the same time, it is important to recognize that maintaining physical fitness in advance of internship is an essential aspect of adaptation. Interns who are physically fit are far less burdened than their out-of-condition colleagues. That good feeling goes with physical fitness is widely known. In addition, the physical effort of carrying out the duties that are imposed by internship requires considerable stamina.

Fitness

Preservation of fitness is conducive to survival and to emotional well being under adverse circumstances. Outstanding evidence of that was widely observed toward the end of the United States' involvement in Viet Nam. Some of the Americans who had been held in Vietnamese prison camps, upon release, were found in surprisingly good condition. Even though they had been kept under very primitive conditions with inadequate food, crude medical care, and various forms of physical and psychological abuse, some of these military people emerged with good morale and relatively intact physical condition. Many of those who had survived in good condition were people who continued to exercise, even though kept in tiny cages. They had exercised for long periods of time every day, by running in place or with other forms of calisthenics, despite their confinement and poor nourishment.

Certain forms of exercise, such as calisthenics, are readily available, even to interns. Opportunities for exercise exist, even within the hospital. Running upstairs, for example, can help maintain muscle tone and aerobic fitness. Stretching exercises and isometric exercises can be performed in offices and on-call rooms. The years of medical school, stressful themselves, invite fitness building. Preparation for internship, optimizing the student's functioning and personal invigoration are shared purposes.

Sexual Behavior

Sexual behavior can, under favorable circumstances, console and restore. It can relieve tension, counteract isolation, neutralize depletion, rebuild morale and restore intimacy.

Arousal may be intensified under stress. More often it is diminished under the typically exhausting conditions of PGYs 1, 2 and beyond. Safety, morality, and opportunity are important limiting factors.

Ill-considered, unwise and impulsive sexuality can make things far worse. A few of the complexities are mentioned in a later chapter (#14). The student's past and current sexual experience can offer guidance regarding his future.

An introspective process analogous to the inventory of coping strategies can be useful in charting a personal course regarding sexual behavior. Discussion with one's partner can be crucial to providing for mutually fulfilling sexual experience in internship (or probably in any phase of life, for that matter). For those without a mate, inner analysis of sexual issues is perhaps more urgent and more challenging.

Nutrition

Remarks about physical factors would be grossly incomplete without at least some reference to nutrition. This is a subject about which medical students usually know a great deal. That knowledge can be applied to the student's own well-being. It is tempting during internship to resort to tasty junk foods that stimulate insulin rebound, add sodium or increase low density lipoprotein. They can also take the place of foods that are far more essential. Many interns use food as a kind of consolation to compensate for other deprivations. If carried too far, this can be self-defeating in terms of adding weight, reducing fitness, impairing physical appearance and consequently harming attitudes about attractiveness and worth.

Building good patterns of nutrition can serve the future intern by making self discipline a bit easier during the difficult times ahead.

References

Agras WS: Eating Disorders: Management of Obesity, Bulimia and Anorexia Nervosa. Oxford, Pergamon, 1987.

Brewster JM: Prevalence of alcohol and other drug problems among physicians. JAMA 1986;255:1913-1920.

Heller RJ, Robertson LS, Alpert JJ: Health care of house officers. N Engl Med 1967;277:907-910.

Herzog DB: Bulimia: The secretive syndrome. Psychosomatics 1982;23:481-487.

Morse DR, Martin JS, Merric LF, et al: A physiological and subjective evaluation of meditation, hypnosis and relaxation. Psychosom Med 1977;39:304-324.

Scott CD, Hawk J, eds. Heal Thyself: The Health of Health Care Professionals. New York, Brunner Mazel, 1986.

Chapter 7

Using Autohypnosis and Relaxation Techniques

Time for sleep is rare and precious for an intern. Nights on call may be uninterrupted periods of intense work. Occasionally the intern or resident may be free to lie down in the on-call room or the back room of the emergency ward. Despite fatigue, he may be so intensely stimulated that he is unable to fall asleep. Thoughts may be racing. There may be concern about patients in a precarious condition but who do not require the intern's immediate efforts. The intern may be apprehensive, expecting to be called at any moment. All of this may prevent sleep or even waking rest.

Remedy For Wakefulness

Many people are able to overcome such wakefulness with one of a host of procedures that can be categorized as autohypnosis. Hypnosis has been a controversial process for centuries. Its applicability to scientific medicine has been debated, and its use has fluctuated. In oriental medicine it has been much more consistently accepted as a useful and respectable process. In occidental medicine its validity has been examined, and considerable evidence of its effectiveness in many situations has been gathered in recent decades. The underlying mechanisms of hypnosis and of autohypnosis remain obscure and controversial.

Relaxation

Related to hypnosis are various forms of relaxation and meditation. These have been studied in elegant fashion by a professor at Harvard Medical School, Herbert Benson, his associates and students, and by others. Demonstrable reduction of blood pressure, pulse rate and respirations have been measured with statistical significance in response to various relaxation and meditation methods.

These positive effects of self-induced relaxation states have been remarkably free of adverse consequences. One of the criticisms of the use of hypnosis in medicine and in other activities has been that it induces an abnormal, or perhaps exploitative, relationship between the hypnotist and his subject. When autohypnosis is employed, such an adverse relationship is precluded.

Of course, one can argue that some sort of internal conflict may be aroused. To my knowledge, such an effect has not been demonstrated. Self-induced hypnotic or relaxation states are safe and effective for many individuals.

The alternatives for the intern are the pain of sleeplessness, tension, fatigue and irritability. Even worse is the danger of sedatives and their abuse.

Substance Abuse By Physicians

Many investigators have reported substantial substance abuse, especially with sedatives, among residents in training and physicians in practice. Initially, interns will avoid taking benzodiazepines while on duty because they fear that their judgment and thinking will not be sufficiently sharp if they are awakened for a subsequent emergency. In fact some of the short acting benzodiazepines are known to induce amnesia covering several hours.

Often, substance abuse begins with efforts to fall asleep when the intern comes off call and is able to go home. The tension and excessive stimulation of the on-call experience may delay or prevent sleep, even after thirty six hours on duty. The dread of having to go back on duty the following morning without some sleep is sometimes sufficiently oppressive to induce the intern to take a benzodiazepine, alcohol or other sedating agents. Such practices can become habitual and, eventually, addictive.

Procedures For Autohypnosis

Autohypnosis is a safe, convenient procedure for inducing sleep and for reducing emotional and physiological tension. The procedures vary, but have several features in common. The first is a comfortable physical position. For meditation and relaxation this is a sitting or partially reclining position. For sleep, a supine position is desirable. Some prefer to have their feet elevated. A small lump of cloth, such as a rolled towel or pillow case, can be slipped under the lumbar curve for support and reduced tension on the muscles of the lower back.

Second is a procedure for trying to clear one's mind of intrusive distracting, or anxiety-producing thoughts. This can be achieved by various methods. One is to try to imagine oneself in a very pleasant surrounding: a site in the woods, at the seashore, or whichever place is enjoyable for the individual to contemplate. Another method is to focus on one's own breathing. Along with this concentration on the respiratory cycle may be the inclusion of a simple thought, sound, or word. With each expiration the subject can think "one", or "out" or a meaningless syllable. This focus is intended to compete with other thoughts that might be stimulating or troubling. Such thoughts may intrude despite the focus on respiration. When that occurs, a variety of relatively calm, passive phases can be used to try to counter them. For example, one might think "not now", or "perhaps later", or "away." Each person can select a phrase that he finds useful.

The third feature is an image of one's body with an associated sense of relaxation. One may start, for example, with a mental picture of one's toes, with the idea, "My toes are relaxed", or "My toes are falling asleep", depending upon the objective of the procedure. Then one thinks, "My feet are relaxed (or falling asleep)", and so on, with the various segments of the body to the shoulders, fingers, arms, neck, head, mind, eyes, eyelids. Another variant is to imagine a wave of relaxation that starts with the toes and moves and flows upward, with a sense that the parts over which the wave is flowing are either relaxing or falling asleep. One person described a soft sleeve of mist that rolled up his legs, trunk, arms, neck and head as he requested it silently. The mist relaxed and sedated all that it enclosed.

This process may seem strange. It can be viewed as a variant of the internal dialogue that was mentioned in a previous chapter (#4). The hypnotic directions, or instructions, can be imagined as a part of the self talking to the remainder of the self. The suggester can be fantasized to be someone whom one respects, whose image is comforting.

The fourth feature of these procedures is autosuggestion. One can suggest relaxation or sleep, or any other comparable word or idea that the subject prefers. In addition, other suggestions may be added. For example, "When I am awakened, I will feel refreshed, energetic, and alert." (see Table 7.1).

Learning and practicing such technics can be aided by a variety of audio tapes available in many music, book or video stores. Finding one that suits one's individual preference may take some experimentation. They can be brought to a hospital on-call room for use on a portable tape player with earphones. Such tapes may require ten minutes to the better part of an hour. Anyone can produce his own.

Silent meditation as a form of sedation can be brief: two or three minutes or less, depending on skill, practice, extent of sleep deprivation and other factors.

None of this is magical. These procedures work more or less well for many people and can become more effective with practice. Skill in relaxing or hypnotizing one's self can be cultivated.

If the resident experiments with the methods described above, he is likely to tailor a technique most effective for himself. He may find other applications for these procedures: to relax prior to performing a surgical procedure, or to reduce anticipatory anxiety prior to a presentation at grand rounds. The student may find uses for it in tension provoking personal situations as well.

References

Asken MJ, Raham DC: Resident performance and sleep deprivation: A review. J Med ED 1983;58:382-388.

Beary JF, Benson H: A simple psychophysiologic technique which elicits the hypometabolic changes of the relaxation response. Psychosomatic Med 1974;36:115-120.

Benson H: Decreased alcohol intake associated with the practice of meditation. Ann NY Acad Sci 1974;233:174-177.

Benson H: Your innate asset for combating stress. Harvard Business Review 1974;52(4):49-60.

Benson H, Beary JF, Carol MP: The relaxation response. Psychiatry 1974;37:37-46.

Benson H, Klipper MZ: The Relaxation Response. New York, Morrow, 1975.

Deaconson TF, O'Hair DP, Levy MF, et al: Sleep deprivation and resident performance. JAMA 1988;260:1721-1727.

Erickson MH, Ross EL: Experiencing Hypnosis. New York, Irvington, 1981.

Friedman RC, Bigger JT, Kornfeld DS: The intern and sleep loss. N Engl J Med 1971;285:201-203.

Friedman RC, Kornfeld DS, Bigger TJ: Psychological problems associated with sleep deprivation in interns. J Med Educ 1973;48:436-441.

Goleman D: The Varieties of Meditative Experience. New York, Dutton, 1977.

Hawkins MR, Vichick DA, Silsby HD et al: Sleep deprivation and performance of house officers. J Med Educ 1985;60:530-535.

McCall TB: The impact of long working hours on resident physicians N Engl J Med 1988;318:775-778.

McCall TB: Sleep deprivation and performance of residents. JAMA 1989;261:859.

Morse DR, Martin JS, Merrick LF, et al: A physiological and subjective evaluation of meditation, hypnosis and relaxation. Psychosom Med 1977;39:304-324.

Pawel BR: Sleep deprivation and resident performance. JAMA 1989;261:860.

Ritchie K: Sleep deprivation and performance of residents. JAMA 1989;261:859-860.

Schwartz CE: Sleep deprivation and performance of residents. JAMA 1989;261:859.

Wallace RK: Physiological effects of transcendental meditation. Science 1970;167:1751-1754.

Wallis C, Crooks C, Hull J: Re-examining the 36-hour day. Time, August 31, 1987.

Waring EM: Psychiatric illness in physicians: A review. Compr Psychiatry 1974;15:519-530.

TABLE 7.1 – Procedures for Autohypnosis

- Assume a comfortable physical position
- Empty consciousness of extraneous thoughts
  - By focusing attention on expiratory phase of respiration
  - With mental repetition of a syllable or word
  - By passive dismissal of intrusive thoughts with
    - "Not now"
    - "Later"
    - "Away"
- Imagine the body and its parts falling asleep
  - By segments
  - In a flow or wave
- Apply suggestions to bring on sleep or to enhance refreshment

---

Chapter 8

Preparing Family and Friends

Looking ahead to internship, the student can expect that its great demands on time, energy and attention will affect his family and friends. The physical availability and personal involvement that the intern can bring to bear toward the people with whom he is intimate are bound to be reduced. Changes in his actions and moods will affect them, and their reactions will very likely be reflected back. Much may be gained by thinking through these expectable changes. After sorting them out mentally, it can help to bring them to the attention of those who are close and important, well in advance. By doing so, the student may be able to forestall substantial disappointments and conflicts. It may lead to development of mutually acceptable ways for coping with the problems. Such collaborative effort can protect the intern and all that the relationships mean to him.

Parents, siblings, spouse, lover, even relatively casual acquaintances with whom the student may be sharing an apartment or house, will know that he has to work hard in medical school. They will be aware that, on occasion, the student may study all night before an examination. In general, they will have some expectations of his behavior, as the student will of theirs.

Duty Precludes Choice

Few people outside the profession of medicine itself fully appreciate the intensity and chronicity of absorption that postgraduate training brings. The all night work sessions may come two or three times a week for months, sometimes for years, with little interruption. They may not recognize that once the internship begins, some of the young doctor's choices are removed. Whereas the medical student may choose to study all night to prepare for an exam, the intern has no such choice when on call. Duty and personal devotion to patient care do not allow for the luxury of stopping at some point in the early morning and deciding to call it a night.

This combination, a work week exceeding one hundred hours and the involuntary quality of some of the most intense parts of it, is rare except in combat situations. There is evidence that young people in other fields, such as law or business, who are ambitious and work in highly pressured jobs, may devote extremely long hours to their occupations. Their efforts may also carry considerable responsibility but rarely require continuous duty for more than twenty four hours. Those people probably need to prepare in comparable ways for their professional development. However, other than medicine, no profession requires around-the-clock work periods five to fifteen times a month for years. The supremely challenging feature of the intern's work is that it affects so directly, and often profoundly, the health and survival of human beings.

Briefings About Internship

It is important for the people who are emotionally significant to the intern to learn about these conditions. Knowing them cognitively, however, is not sufficient. Somehow they must be prepared for the emotional impact on them of the intern's responsibilities and subsequent fatigue and unavailability.

Generally this is best accomplished by explanations and descriptions offered by the student to his loved ones. Some people might benefit by making a visit to the emergency room to observe the intensity of the activities there and to talk to attending physicians or house officers, if that can be arranged. Others may benefit from reading books about postgraduate training, providing that they are authentic. Some may derive benefit from watching motion pictures or from reading magazine articles and other popular descriptions of the circumstances of house officer training. Discussions of the subject with physicians who are relatives or personal friends can also vitalize the description of the circumstances of training. The family physician can help in this regard if he is willing to take the time to do so. An especially effective demonstration can result if they will stay awake with the student for twenty four hours on a long week-end or vacation. This is not encouraged for people who are infirm.

71

Anticipation Of Unavailability

Expectations about social activities with the intern will have to be modified. The intern himself will want to engage in the enjoyable aspects of those relationships and may even rely upon them more than ever for emotional sustenance. This will conflict with his own inability, at times, to contribute his usual share to the relationship. The intern may not have time to make phone calls, write letters, show consideration or perform the day-to-day chores that have been part of an ongoing relationship. He may not have the patience to listen or the equanimity to empathize at times of personal exhaustion.

Lovers, spouses, relatives, siblings, and parents may be disappointed, feel hurt, respond with anger, or simply withdraw, if they are confronted with these changes unprepared. To the intern, these responses may feel like rejections or punishments. They may be perceived as conditions imposed upon him. Conditional love is a form of coercion and may be painful or antagonizing. If these adverse reactions occur while the internship is in full swing, conflict and disruption can ensue. It is very difficult for interns and their loved ones to talk calmly when both sides are distraught and irritable under pressure. The consequence may be a deterioration of the relationship, at least temporarily, and all the participants may suffer intensely.

If such changes in the relationship are discussed before the internship begins, then plans can be made about how all will try to respond cooperatively. They can set, as a joint goal, that the relationship and the individuals will not only survive but will prosper. Next, it is important that both people, or all of the people involved, if possible, pledge explicitly to work collaboratively to achieve this objective. Development of the specific methods can then proceed.

Procedures

Various procedures can be useful. Examples are:

(1) Agreement to notify each other far in advance of events that can be planned,

(2) Telephone conversations can be scheduled,
(3) Chores may be delegated temporarily to others.

A particularly important factor is the delay of serious discussions until the intern has had some rest. Very often the presentation of family or household problems to an intern who is returning from 30-40 hours of continuous duty can be highly counterproductive for both sides. Of course, a concomitant part of such an agreement or delay is that the intern will be willing to engage in the discussion once he has had some rest. It is well known that some young physicians (as well as others who are not so young) will try to postpone important discussions indefinitely, using the pressure of work as a rationalization.

Specifics Involving Mates

It is usually insufficient merely to agree to a joint objective. It is necessary to look at some of the specifics, both emotional and practical. A lot depends upon the nature of the relationship, of course. Plans between a husband and wife are bound to differ from plans made by roommates or housemates. Between people who are sharing a living space for convenience or for financial reasons, the main considerations may be the practical ones: who does the dishes; who takes out the trash; who pays the phone bill? But a social relationship exists nonetheless, and irritability or cordiality are influential.

Among friends, relatives or spouses, availability, especially in difficult times, becomes extremely important and these times need to be anticipated. With mutual goals and a pledge of alliance, methods for solving emotional or practical issues can often be found.

Additional help and guidance can often be obtained for the resident's mate. Virtually all national, state and county medical societies have auxiliaries. Many teaching hospitals have support groups for house officers' spouses and lovers. In addition, most of these organizations have useful handbooks or brochures that provide information, advice and perspective. Resources provided by these organizations can be of great value, and are usually readily available along with the care and concern of many of the senior participants. With their many virtues, they can augment but

73

not fully substitute for communication between the student or resident and his mate.

Just as mental rehearsal is important in anticipating specific features of internship, it is also useful in anticipating discussions with one's spouse or friends. The other person's individual needs and interests are major considerations. Awareness of them will facilitate effective collaboration. They are essential ingredients of joint and mutual objectives. Thinking through some of these issues in advance may prepare the way for more comfortable and successful conversations. (see Table 8.1).

In making these plans with intimates, the medical student or resident may be helped by having a clear idea of his own resources and vulnerabilities. Equally, it can be beneficial to have an explicit idea of the strengths and sensitivities of the lover or friend. The next chapter will introduce ways of looking at such qualities.

References

Barlow E: Rites of residency: New age stresses on the iron intern. Harvard Med Alumni Bull 1989;62(3):36-41.

Coombs RH, Hovanessian HC: Stress in the role constellation of female resident physicians. J Am Med Wom Assoc 1988;43:21-27.

Crouch M: Working with one's own family: Another path for professional development. Fam Med 1986;18:93-98.

Gabbard GO, Menninger RW: The psychology of postponement in the medical marriage. JAMA 1989;261:2378-2381.

Gilligan C: In a Different Voice. Cambridge, Mass, Harvard University Press, 1982.

Landau C, Hall S, Waitman SA, et al: Stress in social and family relationships during medical residency. J Med Educ 1986;61:654-660.

Mengel MB: Physicians' ineffectiveness due to family-of-origin issues. Fam Systems Med 1987;5:176-190.

Miller JB: Toward a New Psychology of Women. Boston, Beacon Press, 1978.

Meyers MF: Marital distress among resident physicians. Can Med Assoc J 1986;134:1117-1118.

Myers MF: Doctors' Marriages: A Look at the Problems and Their Solutions. New York, Plenum, 1988.

Nelson FG, Henry WF: Psychosocial factors seen as problems by family practice residents and their spouses. J Fam Pract 1978;6:581-589.

Pekkanen J: Doctors Talk About Themselves. New York, Delacorte Press, 1988.

Reuben DB: Psychologic effects of residency. Southern Med J 1983;76:380-383.

Small GW: House officer stress syndrome. Psychosomatics 1981;22:860-869.

Smith JW, Denny WF, Witzke DB: Emotional impairment in internal medicine house staff. JAMA 1986;255:1155-1158.

Tokarz JP, Bremer W, Peters K: Beyond Survival. Chicago, AMA 1979.

TABLE 8.1 – Preparing Family and Friends

- Select people to prepare

- Rehearse mentally

- Explain conditions to be expected

- Illustrate, if necessary, with books, films or other means

- Choose goals jointly

- Choose methods collaboratively

Chapter 9

Personal Strengths And Vulnerabilities

To varying degrees we have a sense of our personal strengths and our vulnerabilities. The purpose of reviewing them and making them explicit is to see whether we can invigorate ourselves or recruit additional resources. At the same time, making an inventory of our vulnerabilities may enable us to diminish them, or to find more efficient, less burdensome forms of self-protection.

Strengths

Holding a mirror up to our own personalities may quickly reveal evaluations of our own depth of knowledge, of skills, emotional fortitude, physical strength, values, or positive qualities of personality. Judgment of these factors tends to be highly subjective. We can gain some perspective by trying to discover how we have arrived at them. To what extent were they derived from acceptance and love by parents or other family members; opinions of teachers and friends; or from inner sources? We can also look at whether our judgments were based on performance.

The review of past stresses in Chapter 3 can be used here to introduce objectivity. Looking at the qualities that we view as strengths, how did they serve us in the acute or chronic stresses of past? How did a capacity for learning, physical skills, or capacity to make friends, as examples, influence adaptation to those stresses? With this kind of review, we can then estimate how those qualities may apply under the conditions of internship.

Personal strengths are not measurable exclusively by their capacity to help us in conditions of stress. Some of them add joy and meaning to our lives, provide us with pleasure and provide others with satisfaction. One of the difficulties imposed by internship is that it restricts opportunities to exercise some of our social and cultural interests. For an artist, an excellent athlete, or a contemplative person who likes to think, to talk and to spend easy time with others, the conditions of internship may add frustrations. This is something that we need to anticipate, and we do well to prepare methods for adaptation to those restrictions.

Vulnerabilities

One's view of vulnerabilities can be organized in a manner parallel to the inventory of strengths. Most people are somewhat sensitive to rejection. Many of us who are ambitious enough to enter the field of medicine have some concern about failure since we engage in competitive efforts like applications to schools. There may be some dread of being envied, or discomfort at our envy of others. Many of us experience distress in relation to anger: our own anger at others and the anger of others toward ourselves. Taking these four common—though far from comprehensive—sets of feelings, we may, by looking at ourselves carefully, find that we are particularly sensitive to one or more. By reviewing one's own experience the list may be enlarged.

Vulnerability is here defined as an intensely troubled response to relationships, circumstances or events. These may be connected with ordinary experiences such as meeting people socially, expressing affection, accepting help, or interacting with people who are emotionally needy.

The response may take the form of an intense dysphoria. This can include shame, envy, rage, dread, or a sense of failure. It may be experienced as unpleasant or disturbing thoughts, images or impulses. It could provoke behavior that is, by the subject's standards, unsatisfactory. It might arouse somatic symptoms such as headache, lightheadedness, or any form of autonomic discharge such as rapid pulse, sweating, shakiness, nausea, diarrhea or vomiting. It might produce one or more paresthesias. It can even lead to impaired social or professional functioning, as evaluated by objective measures.

Automatic protective mechanisms may insulate the subject from awareness of his vulnerabilities. Often, the defenses are more easily recognized or are more obvious than are the vulnerabilities themselves. Recognition of the presence of somewhat costly defenses can offer clues to the underlying problems.

One common form of defense against awareness of intense dysphorias is an unreasonable or extremely intense dislike of people who express, exemplify, or provoke those feelings. These might be people who represent or generate feelings of shame, inadequacy, fear, sense of failure, or any of the other intensely dysphoric emotions.

Disinterest in people and activities that might be enriching may be a defense. Aversion to experiences that might be useful or strengthening is an attitude to be questioned. Avoidance of people or activities that might be gratifying or might fulfill a duty is another possible defense. Distraction from spouse, family or profession to a noticeable degree needs to be looked at carefully. Challenge or hostility when friendliness or collegiality might be appropriate invites further autognosis. Aggressiveness or overactivity when calmness might be in order is also to be examined. Failure to accomplish tasks that one judges to be useful or desirable is another possible defense. Excessive involvement in activities that one judges to be undesirable is, of course, an obvious possibility as a costly and maladaptive defense.

Defenses are commonly developed early in life, and may be learned from family members who themselves are in trouble. They may also be improvised under stress or conditions of childhood dependency and weakness. Thinking them through with relative objectivity from the point of view of the mature adult may lead to a new perspective. Autognostic review might lead to discovery of less costly methods of self protection (see Tables 9.1 and 9.2).

Some personal qualities are sources of both strength and of vulnerability. Feminine gender is an outstanding example. Women students, even at present, are still the objects of adverse prejudice in medicine, as well as in other professions, and they have the additional disadvantage of a shorter reproductive life than do men. The twenties and early thirties are the safest childbearing years and simultaneously the period of most intense medical education and training. Child rearing still demands far more time and devotion from a mother than from even a caring and empathic father in most families. A woman in medicine must generate the energy and attention required by two occupations that can each demand full time, if she is to raise children while training. If bearing children is postponed for any reason, biological risks may increase.

Women surgical house officers are at a disadvantage in being excluded from the men's locker room in those services in which the majority of the senior surgeons are male. Showering and dressing after surgery provide opportunities for conversation and bonding. Much information is exchanged. The operation may be reviewed. Many other subjects of professional importance may come up at such times. There is an intimacy in the dressing room that is familiar to most physicians. Those who have engaged in sports have probably known this comradeship.

At the present time, surgical specialties are still dominated by men. Therefore this disadvantage of being excluded continues to handicap women surgeons in training.

However, women tend to be more effective and capable in many areas of interpersonal relatedness than are men. They enjoy greater longevity, and perhaps greater flexibility in adjusting to personal stresses.

Similarly, black students encounter adverse prejudice in and out of medicine. A black house officer was the only member of his race in a prestigious training program. On several occasions he was mistaken for an attendant or a nursing assistant and was asked to perform their relatively menial work. Black students are more likely than white students to have experienced poverty and educational disadvantage.

On the other hand, they have had to overcome those challenges and have added strength and gratification to show for it. Black students and members of ethnic or religious minorities may also bear the pride and responsibility of serving as pathfinders for their families or their communities. Serving as the hope of others may be an important source of encouragement. It may also prove a burden, because the price of failure might be paid not only by the student, but also by the family or community.

These examples are offered to illustrate the complexity of even the most obvious personal traits. Each individual student has the opportunity to examine in detail the exquisite complexity of his own personality in terms of what may be helpful in internship and what may be an impediment to functioning.

Helpful and Troubling Relationships

The concept of being a favorite son or daughter — or representative of a community that goes beyond one's own family — brings up another dimension of strengths and vulnerabilities. This includes the relationships that one can call upon for sustenance or the relationships that serve as depleting responsibilities to the student. The resources available to the student are usually not limited to himself. There are others who can be sought for collaboration. That roster needs to be examined in detail to determine who might help and who might hinder, especially during internship.

A survey conducted mentally will usually call forth friends, relatives and others who can provide encouragement, companionship, comfort or various forms of practical help. It will also probably find those to whom the student feels duty or responsibility. For the latter, the student may be able to get some assistance from the former. The potentially supportive friends and relatives may at least be able to provide ideas, points of view or perspective on how to fulfill one's personal duties while subject to the demands of internship.

An appraisal of one's personal qualities can be aided by discussion with friends or even more objective confidants. This has been demonstrated in a seminar devoted to autognosis which I have been privileged to lead for twenty years. The participants have been first year residents in psychiatry, most of whom had not known each other before entering the training program.

Evaluation of the factors mentioned here can be carried out through simple introspection with the addition, perhaps, of internal dialogue. Many students may benefit from a written list. While a number of these features will be self-evident to the student and will come to mind instantly upon reading this, others may be hidden away for reasons of sensitivity or emotional pain. Some of them might emerge at a later time and can be considered then.

Contemplation of one's non-professional involvements and recreational activities can be revealing. If interests in music, photography, drama, travel or sports are examined closely, they can illuminate much that is essential. They can tell a great deal about significant events or trends in personal history, and how traits of personality were shaped. They can inform about qualities like perserverence, optimism, idealism and ability to manage success or disappointment. Hobbies often tap into profoundly personal tendencies. Times at which those interest arose or declined may signal important nodal points in personal development.Students vary in the detail to which they will subject these matters to personal scrutiny. That, too, is a matter of personal preference and style. The standard that may be useful for many students is preparation for internship. Has the student's examination of his strengths and vulnerabilities been sufficient to assure their effective deployment in the internship experience? (see Table 9.3).

The review of personal assets and liabilities can be extended even beyond one's traits and relationships with other people. It can include avocations, sports, finances and religious involvement. Techniques for applying this broader view are offered next.

References

Beauchamp T, Childress JF: Ideals, virtues and conscientious actions, in Principles of Biomedical Ethics. New York, Oxford University Press, 1983.

Blackwell B: Prevention of impairment among residents in training. JAMA 1986;255:1177-1178.

Borenstein DB, Cook K: Impairment prevention in the training years: A new mental health program at UCLA. JAMA 1982;247:2700-2703.

Brewster JM: Prevalence of alcohol and other drug problems among physicians. JAMA 1986;255:1913-1920.

Bronner E: The foot soldiers of medicine. The Boston Sunday Globe Magazine, July 6, 1986.

Clark DC, Zeldow PB: Vicissitudes of depressed mood during four years of medical school. JAMA 1988;260:2521-2528.

Coombs RH, Hovanessian HC: Stress in the role constellation of female resident physicians. J Am Med Wom Assoc 1988;43:21-27.

Dubovsky SL, Schrier RW: The mystique of medical training: Is teaching perfection in medical house-staff training a reasonable goal or a precursor of low self esteem? JAMA 1983;250:3057-3058.

Figley CR, ed: Trauma and Its Wake. New York, Brunner Mazel, 1985.

Flannery RB: The stress-resistant person. Harvard Med School Health Letter 1989;14(4):5-7.

Gaensbauer TJ, Mizner GL: Developmental stresses in medical education. Psychiatry 1980;43:60-70.

Herzog DB: Bulimia: The secretive syndrome. Psychosomatics 1982;23:481-487.

Kohner M. Becoming a Doctor: A Journey of Initiation in Medical School. New York, Penguin Books, 1988.

Kris K: Developmental strains of women medical students. J Am Med Wom Assoc 1985;40:145-148.

Miller JB: Toward a New Psychology of Women. Boston, Beacon Press, 1978.

Pepitone-Arreola-Rockwell F, Rockwell D, Core N: Fifty-two medical student suicides. Am J Psychiatry 1981;138:198-201.

Pfifferling JH, Blum JC, Wood W: The prevention of physician impairment. J Fla Med Assoc 1981;68:268-273.

Reuben DB: Psychologic effects of residency. Southern Med J 1983;76:380-383.

Reuben DB: Depressive symptoms in medical house officers. Arch Intern Med 1985;145:286-288.

Rich CL, Pitts FN: Suicide by male physicians during a five year period. Am J Psychiatry 1976;136:1089-1090.

Ritchie K: Sleep deprivation and performance of residents. JAMA 1989;261:859-860.

Salmons PH: Psychiatric illness in medical students. Br J Psychiatry 1983;143:505-508.

Schwartz CE: Sleep deprivation and performance of residents. JAMA 1989;261:859.

Scott CD, Hawk J, eds. Heal Thyself: The Health of Health Care Professionals. New York, Brunner Mazel, 1986.

Shapiro E, Lowenstein L, eds: Becoming a Physician: Development of Values and Attitudes in Medicine. Cambridge, MA Allinger, 1979.

Sharaf M, Levinson D: The quest for omnipotence in professional training. Int J Psychiatry 1967;4:426-454.

Sheehan KH, Sheehan DV, White K, et al: A pilot study of medical student "abuse": Student perceptions of mistreatment and misconduct in medical school. JAMA 1990;263:533-537.

Siegel B, Connelly JC: Enriching personal and professional development: The experience of a support group for interns. J Med Educ 1978;53:908-914.

Silver HK, Glicken AD: Medical student abuse: Incidence, severity and significance. JAMA 1990;263:527-532.

Silver RL, Wortzman CB: Coping with undesirable life events. In Garber J, Seligman MEP, eds: Human Helplessness. New York, Academic Press 1980.

Smith JW, Denny WF, Witzke DB: Emotional impairment in internal medicine house staff. JAMA 1986;255:1155-1158.

Stein HF: The Psychodynamics of Medical Practice. Berkeley, University of California Press, 1985.

Vaillant GE, Sobowale NC, McArthur C: Some psychologic vulnerabilities of physicians. N Engl J Med 1972;287:372-375.

Valko RJ, Clayton PJ: Depression in internship. Dis Nerv Syst 1975;36:26-29.

Victoroff VM: My dear colleague: Are you considering suicide? JAMA 1985;254:3464-3466.

Wallis C, Crooks C, Hull J: Re-examining the 36-hour day. Time, August 31, 1987.

Zabarenko R, Zabarenko L: The Doctor Tree: Development Stages in the Growth of Physicians. Pittsburgh, University of Pittsburgh Press, 1978.

TABLE 9.1 — Indicators of Vulnerability

- Intense dysphoria:
  - Shame
  - Envy
  - Feelings of inadequacy, failure or worthlessness
  - Rage
  - Fear of envy by others
  - Fear of alienation or rejection
  - Fear of the anger of others
  - Dread of violence
- Unpleasant or disturbing thoughts, images or impulses
- Unsatisfactory behavior by one's own standards
- Somatic symptoms:
  - Headache
  - Lightheadedness
  - Autonomic discharge
- Impaired functioning as measured by objective standards

TABLE 9.2 – Costly Protective Methods

- Dislike of people who express, exemplify, or evoke feelings that are found disturbing
- Disinterest in people and activities that might be enriching
- Aversion to experiences that might be useful or strengthened
- Avoidance of people or activities that might be gratifying or might fulfill a duty
- Distraction from spouse, family or profession
- Challenge or hostility where friendliness or collegiality might be appropriate
- Aggressive or overactive behavior where calmness might be more satisfactory
- Not accomplishing tasks that one judges to be useful or desirable
- Doing too much of activities that one judges to be undesirable

TABLE 9.3 – Evaluation of Strengths and Vulnerabilities

- Methods
  - Introspection
  - Lists
  - Discussion with:
    - Intimates
    - Objective but knowledgeable confidants
- Productive sources for review
  - Ready knowledge of self
  - Responses to stresses
  - Gratifying achievements
  - Disappointing experiences
  - Painful relationships
  - Social roles and expectations

Chapter 10

The Best Times of Your Life

If the reader thinks back to the best times of his life, several memories may arise. He might recall several particularly outstanding events or sequences, perhaps only one. Their duration can be moments or years, months or days. The criteria for judging these experiences will be chosen by the reader. The selection can be made in terms of personal fulfillment, learning, joy, intimacy, happiness, poignancy, achievement, self discipline, or any meaningful quality.

If these heights are examined closely, it may be possible to find ways to reproduce them in part or at least symbolically. In the internship experience, this will require ingenuity in most instances. We can analyze the experiences in terms of people, places, things, and activities.

People

The people who were involved in those happy times may still be part of the student's life. If they are living with the student, then collaboratively the superlative times may be reproducible. If those people are living at a a distance, they can be called by telephone, or written correspondence can be renewed. Even if the other participants in those valued experiences are no longer living, then mementos, photographs or other means for recollection can be introduced in a prominent way in the intern's living situation.

Valued friendships that may have lapsed can be revived. Contacts with distant family members can be reactivated. Letters, recordings, or photographs can be made a prominent part of the current and future situation.

Places

Places that were important can be revisited. They can be seen directly or in photographs. In some instances, one can read books about them. Even if those places are geographically distant, they can be brought closer in some way symbolically or through contact with people who still reside there.

Things

Things that played an important role in the best times may be retained. They may be books or photographs, furniture, sports equipment, trophies or manuscripts. If these objects are present, they can be used as the focus of memory.

Activities

Activities reminiscent of the better times may be capable of being continued, even in the internship year. They may be somewhat remote if they were sailing, fishing, hunting, mountain climbing, or international travel. It may be possible to engage in some of them briefly during vacations, but they may be kept closely available through books, photographs, videotapes, or other forms of recording. The cherished activities may be kept active through communication with people who are able to participate in those activities, in the present, while the intern is prevented from access to them.

The activities need not be confined to matters of fun and relaxation. It could be that they were religious moments in which the intern can continue to participate. The best times may consist of teaching disadvantaged children; building furniture for impoverished families; providing advocacy for victims of mental retardation; or reading to the blind. Some of those activities can be continued, if only in attenuated forms, during internship; even a few hours every week or two, or every month, may be sufficient to revive the profound satisfaction that they provided in times past.

If the resident examines the zeniths, he is likely to find ways to revitalize those experiences, even in the strenuous and austere period of internship. He may find creative combinations of activities or relationships that will recapture what was valuable in the past. He may create something equally good, or better, that will be available regularly in the first postgraduate year.

Many students rely upon memory and the benefits of their constructive past to sustain and strengthen themselves. It may appear unnecessary to utilize the analysis of this chapter because the best can be recalled. In many instances, this is true, but the absorption that internship often inflicts may require something beyond mere recall. The employment of relationships, mementos and the other devices may be necessary to help the intern climb out of the pit of stress in which he finds himself.

Sustained by connections with the pinnacles of his life, the intern will be in a better position to cope with what comes his way. He may be less vulnerable then to the calcifying and misanthropic attitudes that are sometimes awakened or evoked in young physicians. He may then be able to work with his patients in the humane and compassionate manner that his genuine impulses direct. Revival of the best times may contribute strength for managing the quantity of work and the behavior of patients, which are often difficult.

References

Horowitz MI: Image Formation and Psychotherapy. New York, Jason Aronson, 1983.

Internship: Physicians Respond to Norman Cousins. JAMA 1981;246:2141-2144.

Morris PE, Hampson PJ: Imagery and Consciousness. New York, Academic Press, 1983.

Rotbart HA, Nelson WL, Krantz J, et al: The developmental process of residency education. Issues of stress and happiness. Am J Dis Child 1985;139:762-765.

Singer JL: Imagery and Day Dreaming Methods in Psychotherapy and Behavior Modification. New York, Academic Press, 1984.

Yager J: Teaching guided imagery. Academic Psychiatry 1989;13:31-38.

Chapter 11

Managing Difficult Behavior By Patients

Patient care is the main activity of the intern. While we are sometimes focused on injuries, diseases and pathological processes, it is the person who is suffering who is actually the object of our concern as physicians. Probably most of us who enter the profession of medicine do so at least in part because we have a strong desire to reduce suffering, preserve health, and prolong vitality. For some, these intentions have profound significance.

Physicians' Expectations

Our expectations of patients is that they will want to have their suffering reduced, their disabilities cleared away, and their lives prolonged with comfort and meaning. We often hope that they or others will also appreciate our efforts. We expect and hope that they will at least cooperate with treatment efforts and contribute to their own care.

Circumstances of internship and residency, as well as the complexities of patients' personalities, will sometimes interfere with the fulfillment of our intentions and expectations. Some patients are not only not appreciative and not cooperative in their treatment, but are actually disruptive of their own care, and occasionally of the care of other patients. Interns are frequently confronted by hostile behavior and angry complaints. House officers who experience such unpleasant responses by patients may feel hurt, disappointed, disillusioned, and sometimes even demoralized.

With the strenuous demands of internship, even normal appropriate behavior by patients may impose an additional burden upon the intern. Understandable concerns by a patient about his own condition may seem troublesome when the intern has seven or eight other patients to deal with under conditions of urgency, especially after a long night on call. Interest and concern by the patient's relatives, even when presented politely, may seem burdensome because of the shortage of time. Expectable emotional expressions by the patient or his relatives — feelings of sadness,

89

fear, or dread—may be experienced by the intern as an additional chore with which he must cope.

Difficult Behavior Defined

For the purpose of this presentation, difficult behavior is defined as the intern's perception of it. In assessing such behavior, the judgment first should be made whether or to what extent it feels difficult because of the intern's own state of depletion.

Reasonable Test For Maladaptive Behavior

Even if the patient's behavior is entirely appropriate, it presents a task for the intern to assimilate along with all the rest of his agenda. The purpose of this chapter is to find ways for the intern to cope with difficult behavior by patients, regardless of whether the difficulty stems primarily from the patient or his family or is largely a consequence of the intern's vulnerability. If the patient's behavior would be considered reasonable and appropriate to the patient's circumstance in the judgment of a detached observer, we can anticipate that reasonable responses from the intern would move toward a solution of the problem. If the patient's behavior is difficult as a consequence of a maladaptive feature of the patient's personality or a quirk of his circumstances, a purely reasonable response by the intern may well not solve the problem. Our twin objectives in these considerations are to provide the best possible patient care and to reduce superfluous stress on the intern. In most instances, the two goals coincide. Occasionally they may be competitive.

Forms Of Difficult Behavior

Difficult patient behavior may impact the intern through one or more of the following:

- Intense emotions expressed vocally
- Demands expressed vocally
- Non-compliance
- Manipulation
- Disruptive conduct

90

Developing Collaborative Relationships

A bit later we shall look at approaches to remedying the situation or finding effective steps toward solution of the patient's underlying problem. Before that, a few remarks about establishing basic rapport and a collaborative relationship may be useful. Most residents have a natural inclination toward developing effective relationships with patients. These attitudes and personal traits are reinforced by courses and seminars, given at a great many schools, to enhance doctor-patient relationships. Since the personal traits and the educational experience of readers vary, the following comments are offered.

Courtesy, consideration, compassion and empathy are fundamental attitudes for the physician toward his patients. They contribute substantially to the matrix of this relationship.

From the beginning of any contact with the patient, it is desirable usually to clarify the goal or objective of the medical care. If the patient is not conscious, it can be presented to relatives or whoever accompanies the patient. If the patient is conscious and able to understand his circumstances, it is important to remind him — perhaps repeatedly — that the object of treatment is to reduce pain and to treat the injury or underlying disorder that is causing his symptoms. This may seem superfluous, but such reminders can activate the patient's motivation to cooperate with treatment. It is also important to remind the patient and his family or others who are with the patient, that their collaboration is important, if not essential, for the best possible treatment to take place. They are most likely to cooperate if they are told what needs to be done; why it needs to be done; and exactly what they can do to help.

Some physicians are concerned that inviting collaboration undermines the physician's authority or control. Actually, effective clinical leadership involves explanations and directions while imparting to those who are led the recognition that their contributions are meaningful.

Patient's Individuality

As early as feasible in the doctor-patient relationship, it is valuable to acknowledge the patient's individuality. Many patients find themselves in hospital situations bereft of their familiar surroundings, activities and possessions. They lie in a hospital bed wearing a hospital johnny, with hospital-issued equipment around them, with no one, or nothing that is personal. They are vulnerable to feelings of embarrassment, isolation, humiliation, or devaluation. These conditions evoke defensive or regressive behavior in a substantial percentage of people admitted to hospitals. With patients who are psychologically fragile, such experiences can be pathogenic and may lead to psychiatric symptoms.

These reactions can be modified or neutralized if the patient is approached in a way that will emphasize his individuality. Steps in this direction can be taken very easily by obtaining some personal information about the patient beyond his name. Simple questions like, "Where do you come from?", or "What kind of work do you do?", can offer the patient an opportunity to talk about his own circumstances. It can give him an opportunity to say something as an individual. If what he says is accepted, and an interested question or two are asked, the patient may begin to develop a strong sense of bonding to the clinician. It may also go a long way toward restoring the patient's sense of dignity and individuality which can, in turn, lead to a recruitment of his personal strengths. These may become extremely valuable allies in the treatment that will ensue.

Sometimes, the most ordinary personal item can offer the clinician a clue toward developing more effective rapport. A question about a photograph of someone on the bedside table or about the daily newspaper open to the sports section, the financial section, or a news item, can serve as the springboard for the patient to reveal himself as a unique individual:

"I notice that you are reading about the local basketball team"; or "Who is that little girl whose picture is on the table?"; or "Where were you before you came here?"

Questions such as these can lead to a conversation that may not require more than a minute in actual time, but it can bring a reinforcement of the clinician's relationship with the patient that may save many minutes, or even hours, in the future.

Such interchanges can introduce a continuing topic or theme, in the relationship between the clinician and the patient. If it results in a restoration of the patient's sense of dignity and worth as a person, it will be part of good patient care and will probably lead to increased cooperation with the physician. It will partly satisfy the intern's desire to function as a compassionate doctor and may prevent some of the problems that might otherwise make his work even more difficult.

Expressions of Emotion

One of the main types of appropriate patient behavior that may appear difficult to the intern or resident is the expression of powerful emotions. Intense feelings of pain, apprehension, anguish and grief may arouse unsettling reactions in the intern. He may be vulnerable to one or more of such feelings if his own personal circumstance resonates with what the patient is experiencing. Fatigue and sleep deprivation by themselves can sensitize the physician to strong feeling from others. The emotion that is often most difficult for interns to bear is intense anger, especially if it is directed against the doctor himself.

The clinician may serve as the target for anger that is a response to pain, fear, and the other dysphoric experiences that patients undergo. Sometimes the anger is aroused by a delayed medical procedure or other annoyance experienced in the hospital. A common consequence of anger that the intern has not earned is to antagonize. Such experiences cumulatively may produce hardening of the intern's feelings toward patients. The intern needs to remind himself that he can be the target of feelings without deserving them. They can be painful and unpleasant but are part of the circumstances of hospital experience. To some extent, it is akin to the anguished screams of a frightened and injured child. In adults, regressive actions can be understood but not necessarily excused or condoned.

In some instances, anger may be provoked by a lack of courtesy or consideration on the part of the intern. An acknowledgement, or perhaps even an apology, may be the best way to respond. Patients who are reacting appropriately to their situation will usually be satisfied if their feelings are heard and acknowledged as understandable human responses.

Requests For Information

Request for information and explanations are best met with acknowledgements that these are natural and appropriate questions. The difficulty is that the intern may be too rushed to comply at that moment. If the intern is attempting to provide enough information to allow informed consent for a procedure or treatment, it is essential that time be found to impart the information to the patient and his companions. In many instances, patients will be content to receive a part of the information they are requesting if the intern indicates that he will take time later on to provide the rest. As an alternative, the intern can provide the salient features of the information and delegate the rest of it to a surrogate, such as a medical student or a social worker.

Difficult behavior that emanates from the patient's personal peculiarities, or that of his circumstances, must first be recognized. With disruptive or overtly non-compliant behavior, this is relatively easy.

Maladaptive Behavior

The concept of maladaptation tells us that behavior that undermines the patient's own health, recovery or rehabilitation is inappropriate. Manipulative, demanding, or excessively intense hostile expressions and behavior that antagonizes, alienates, undermines, or abuses the staff, are maladaptive. Even if the hospital staff, including the residents, are able to withstand such machinations and still provide first class care, a self-defeating tendency of the behavior by the patient can be discerned. A fairly general diagnostic test for the irrationality of behavior is simply a considerate, kindly, rational response on the part of the house officer. If that, along with appropriately professional behavior on the part of the nurses and others, fails to move toward a resolution of the difficulty, one can infer that a significant irrational element is present.

Misbehavior As Communication

A useful way to view these irrational, difficult behaviors — intense and harsh vocalizations, excessive emotional expression, demanding behavior, non-compliance, manipulation, or disruptive conduct — is that they are forms of communication. These are signals of a latent message. There is something about the patient that we need to understand in order to manage the situation more effectively.

The hidden messages may be intense and dreadful feelings that the patient is not able to tolerate directly. Examples are terror, apprehension, despair and overwhelming pain. Feelings of weakness and helplessness are sometimes disguised behind a cloud of anger and hostility. Some patients feel so deprived and depleted that they try desperately to get more comfort than the situation can permit. They may try to manipulate to get more of something: attention, medication, reassurance.

Discovering the patient's latent message is often difficult. It is necessary that the clinician look for it actively. If the intern bears in mind the hypothesis that irrational patient behavior represents communication of something hidden, then he is less likely to feel personally attacked. Attuning to non-verbal, paraverbal or symbolic information may enable the intern to bring to bear his cognitive capabilities as a balance to his emotional sensitivity. This view also reminds the clinician that the patient is externalizing something that originates from within. Therefore, his attacks on the medical staff, the hospital, or others, can be seen as a distraction, an attempt to protect his own sensitivities. Obnoxious behavior is distancing behavior. It serves as an insulation or protection, like an emotional moat.

The Clinician's Subjectivity As Data

When the messages are deciphered, they often make a special kind of sense. Sometimes patients manage to evoke in a clinician feelings that are similar to those that the patient experienced: misery that the patient feels in the present or felt in the past. This may serve as a form of revenge against the world or the authority that the patient sees as the source of his suffering. It may be an ambivalent attempt at gaining sympathy while exacting vengeance. It may be a way of saying, "See, this is the way I feel, or the way I felt — now you feel it and can really know what I have been through."

Such processes were originally observed, understood and described in the medical literature as a result of experience in psychoanalysis. Later such observations were observed in psychotherapy and eventually investigated in other doctor-patient encounters.

Complementary Identification

When patients evoke feelings and attitudes in the clinician comparable to the feelings experienced by the patient's parents, the process is referred to as countertransference or complementary identification. For example, the patient may have had a parent who was annoyed when the patient became ill, or who was unsympathetic or uncaring. The patient may expect such responses from the clinician. He may misperceive the clinician's kind and considerate behavior as unsympathetic or irritated. Another process may be that the patient will behave in such a way as to evoke irritation or annoyance by the clinician, thereby replicating the parental relationship. Many patients whose behavior is annoying or distancing belong to this category.

Concurrent Identification

Some patients evoke in the clinician feelings and attitudes that the patient experiences. This process is called projective identification or concurrent identification. The intern may feel frightened, lonely or helpless – probably to an unfamiliar degree – in circumstances related to such patients.

Observation or recognition of one's own subjective experience can sometimes offer a clue to the patient's communication. For example, one student described an encounter with an alcoholic patient who made the student feel frustrated and useless. This raised some questions about whether these were feelings that the patient himself had experienced and was trying to convey to the clinician. Perhaps it was a reversal of roles or an example of projective identification.

Patients who feel empty, deprived, needy, or exhausted, may demand replenishment verbally. Other may attempt it through manipulation.

One form is to reject what is offered in the hope of getting something even better. This is a self-defeating kind of manipulation that manifests as rejection of help or of non-compliance.

Benefits Of Illness

Illness can provide psychological benefits at three levels. The primary gain can be an internal comfort, a feeling of deserving care and attention, and exemption from one's usual effort or from competition. The secondary gain is on an interpersonal level in which one can obtain special attention and care. The tertiary level of gain can be a tangible one in which the individual may actually receive some financial compensation for his medical or surgical condition.

These gains may be far outweighed by the pain, suffering or disability associated with the illness. In some people, the gains exceed the distress imposed by the disabilities. In such circumstances, the patient may have strong motivation, which may be unconscious, to prolong or even to worsen the illness.

Validation Of Subjective Data

It is difficult to be certain about the significance of patients' hidden communications. The subjective experience of the clinician can serve as a signal. It is ordinarily not sufficient as a diagnostic instrument by itself. When the signal feeling is internally perceived by the clinician, then other sources of information can be sought — questions to the patient or to informants who are familiar with the patient. Subjective experiences of the clinician can serve to direct a line of inquiry to validate or to refute the clinical hypotheses that the intern's emotional reaction reveals something abut the patient. This is an example of an autognostic procedure. (see Table 11.1).

When we try to gain additional information about the significance of a patient's overt behavior, we try to translate the patient's actions into verbal content. In doing so, we are most rewarded if we seek the fine details of the patient's history or experience. Generalizations can serve a defensive function. The meaningful features of experience, especially the emotionally laden ones, reside in the small details. A clinician can assist a patient in re-experiencing and expressing his feelings by leading the patient to recall a significant event in the past. For example, if the physician has reason to believe that the death of a relative was particularly significant and led to pent up emotions, he can try to help the patient recall that lost relative. This can be accomplished by asking questions about the last contact that the patient had with his relative. Asking for details of the experience can facilitate the process. The physician can ask, "What did your mother look like at the time?"

"What was she wearing?"

"What was she feeling at that time?"

The patient could also be asked, "What was the mood in the room at the time of your last contact?" Other questions can be, "What did it follow? What happened before?" By pursing questions like why now, or why then, and by prompting sensory recall, the patient's feelings may be brought more readily to the surface. If the patient is asked about sounds or colors, other visual recollections, or even odors or textures, feelings can be evoked with less difficulty.

Patients' Hostility

When confronted by hostile or antagonistic behavior by the patient, we can resort to a checklist that includes a question about whether the clinician himself has earned it, has overlooked something, or has been inattentive or inconsiderate. In some instances, this may be the source of difficulty, but usually we go beyond that to asking what may be the source of the anger, if it is not the overtly labeled object that the patient is attacking. We may ask who or what is the deeply intended target of the antagonism.

If the intern himself is the overt target of hostility, he may need to utilize an expressive fantasy of his own as an emergency procedure. This may serve to discharge enough of the clinician's own feelings to buy time and equanimity for more analytic thinking.

In many situations in which the patient is emotionally aroused, it can be helpful to try to revive the alliance between patient and doctor. This means reminding the patient that the clinician is a member of the treatment team, and the purpose of it is to help the patient with his illness or injury. The patient is also reminded that his collaboration is important to the accomplishment of that treatment goal.

With that reminder it is sometimes possible to help the patient regain some perspective. A useful question is, "From your point of view, what do you think is going on here?" This is an invitation to the patient to make use of his cognitive capabilities and to develop some perspective on the situation. It also acknowledges that the patient's point of view is respected. At the same time, it implies that there may be other points of view.

Seeking Deeper Concerns

The patient may insist that his hostility is justified: that the nurses are slow; the food is cold; or the room is too warm. Without disputing these explanations, the intern can ask whether there is more. Is there anything else that is troubling the patient? Surprisingly, many hostile patients will, in fact, confide about their more personal concerns if the physician asks for more information along these lines. Sometimes the patient will use an outward complaint such as the food or the ambient temperature as a crude invitation or demand for attention to more profound concerns. If the clinician can refrain from disputing or ignoring the patient's gambit, more fundamental concerns may come to the surface.

Translating Behavior Into Words

Another method is to translate the patient's behavior specifically into words and to ask him what he imagines is the effect of his behavior. For example, "You've been yelling at the nurses and insulting them. What do you imagine would be the effect of that kind of behavior? Are trying to punish them? Do you think that this is the way to get them to give you better treatment? What other ways do you know to encourage people to act in a way that is more satisfying to you?"

Hospital Discharge Reactions

The time just prior to the patient's discharge from the hospital is often a period of crisis. Patients may exhibit regressive behavior, hostility, or develop new symptoms. For many patients, their fears or other aversions to going home may lead them to behave in a less mature way than they had until that point. They may become angry at members of the hospital staff or toward the hospital itself. They may have accidents such as falling out of bed. Often, such patients are not consciously aware of the significance of their behavior. Frequently, it can be understood in terms of a desire for continued care, a sense that hospital discharge is a form of rejection. Development of the new symptoms or injuries may serve both to punish the hospital staff as well as to provide additional justification for continued hospitalization.

If recognized by the intern, such behavior is less likely to be disturbing. It can also be anticipated, or even pre-empted, by giving the patient time to prepare himself psychologically for the end of his hospital stay. It is essential to pay attention to the practical needs of the patient with respect to discharge: arrangements for home care, return visits, help from family members or others, and assistance to the patient in coping with those aspects of his situation about which he is concerned. Another helpful procedure in preventing termination problems is to offer the patient an opportunity to verbalize his emotional concerns about leaving. They may overlap but not be entirely congruent with the practical matters. If not heard they may intensify the regression, hostility and new issues.

Disruptive Conduct

Whereas non-compliance leads to impairment of his own treatment, disruptive behavior leads to interference with the functioning of the treatment unit or directly interferes with the treatment or welfare of other patients. Such actions may be divided into two categories. The first is disruptive behavior as a manifestation of some form of dementia. The other is based upon volitional misbehavior.

If dementia is suspected, it should be tested carefully and appropriately. Mental status and a variety of paper and pencil and other behavioral tests can help clarify the extent of dementia. If impairment of brain function is discovered, then its cause needs to be sought. The causes are varied: vascular, metabolic, neoplastic, toxic, or almost any pathophysiologic process. If the underlying cause is discovered, appropriate treatment should be instituted along with restraints that are sufficient to protect the patient and to protect the treatment unit.

Setting Limits

Non-demented or volitional disruptive behavior needs to be treated with appropriate limit-setting. The most effective form of internal limit setting comes from asking the patient to consider the consequences of his behavior. In the absence of sociopathic or conscienceless tendencies, this is often sufficient to lead the patient to discipline himself. This approach can be tested quickly. If the internal restraints do not suffice, then external limits such as rules and authoritative directions need to be tried. In some situations, external mechanical restraints with the assistance of hospital security personnel may have to be employed.

Protective Force

When force must be used to restrain a violent patient, care should be taken to protect him as well as all others involved. This is best accomplished with five to nine trained security people. One should be available to hold and protect the patient's head and neck. At least one is needed for each extremity. The presence of a large detachment of capable workers can have a pacifying effect by itself. Many excited patients, especially males, may feel that they do not need to struggle against a large group to prove their masculinity as they might when faced with only two or three attendants.

The procedure is best coordinated by the physician, usually the intern. He should continue to talk to the patient explaining that restraint is necessary for safety, not to hurt the patient. If the intern can remain calm and not threaten, insult or antagonize the patient, violence and danger may be minimal. Protection of the patient and staff can be maintained, and the patient may actually feel relieved when brought under control.

Summary

A repertoire for establishing collaborative relationships with patients can facilitate diagnostic and treatment processes. If difficult patient behavior cannot be prevented, then viewing such behavior as a form of communication may help the clinician to understand it in ways that might lead to rational management. The suggestions offered constitute the beginning of a collection of interpersonal techniques to which the young physician will add as he gains experience.

References

Balint M: The Doctor, His Patient and the Illness (2nd ed). New York, International Universities Press, Inc., 1972.

Bayer R, Callahan D, Fletcher, et al.: The care of the terminally ill: Mortality and economics. N Engl J Med 1983;309:1490-1494.

Cassell EJ: Talking with Patients: Volume 1. The Theory of Doctor-patient Communication. Cambridge, Mass, MIT Press, 1985.

Cassell EJ: Talking with Patients: Volume 2. Clinical Technique. Cambridge, Mass, MIT Press, 1985.

Chappel JN, Schnoll SH: Physician attitudes: Effect on the treatment of chemically dependent patients. JAMA 1977;237:2318-2319.

Dubin WR, Wilson SJ, Mercer C: Assaults against psychiatrists in outpatient settings. J Clin Psychiatry 1988;49:338-345.

Gorlin R, Zucker HD: Physicians' reactions to patients. N Engl J Med 1983;308:1059-1063.

Groves JE: Taking care of the hateful patient. N Engl J Med 1978;298:883-887.

Kelly JA, St Lawrence JS, Smith S Jr, et al: Medical students' attitudes toward AIDS and homosexual patients. J Med Educ 1987;62:549-556.

Lion JR: Evaluation and Management of the Violent Patient. Springfield IL, Scharles C Thomas, 1972.

Maltsberger JT, Buie DH: Countertransference hate in the treatment of suicidal patients. Arch Gen Psychiatry 1974;30:625-633.

Reynolds RE, Bice TW: Attitudes of medical interns toward patients and health professionals. J Health Soc Behav 1971;12:307-311.

Smith RC: Teaching interviewing skills to medical students: The issue of "countertransference." J Med Educ 1984;59:582-588.

Stein S: The House of God. New York, Dell, 1978.

Tardiff K, Maurice WL: The care of violent patients by psychiatrists. Can Psychiatric Assoc J 1977;22:83-86.

Thackery M: Therapeutics for Aggression. New York, Human Sciences Press, 1987.

Wachter RM: The impact of the acquired immunodeficiency syndrome on medical residency training. N Engl J Med 1986;314:177-180.

TABLE 11.1 — Autognosis in a Clinical Encounter

The Clinician

- Perceives his subjective experience
  - Emotional arousal
  - Fantasy
  - Impulse
  - Somatic sensation
    - Pain
    - Paresthesia
    - Autonomic discharge
  - Spontaneous action
    - Posture
    - Gesture
    - Tone of voice
- Scans its roots and significance in his personal life and professional circumstance
- Considers it as data evoked by his patient
- Formulates a hypothesis about the patient
- Tests the hypothesis with data from other sources
  - A line of questions
  - Other informants and observers
  - Objective information such as
    - Charts
    - Laboratory tests
    - Physical findings
- Confirms, refutes or modifies the hypothesis
- Applies the hypothesis and other data to clinical management

Chapter 12

Peers and Mutual Reinforcement

"It helps to be able to complain, if only to peers," said one student. Numerous students, interns and residents have made such comments to me. Commiseration is comforting, a phenomenon not confined to the medical profession. Griping comes naturally and provides relief to people under stress.

The mutual sympathy that peers can provide is one of the main sources of sustenance for interns and residents. Friendship, mutual concern and collaboration can go far in helping interns manage their difficult assignments. They cover for each other to permit management of important personal matters or when urgent duties require the intern to be in two or more places at once.

In view of the importance of these supportive and helpful relationships, it is vital that a collaborative atmosphere be maintained in the internship group. Some individuals are naturally better team players than others; some are relative loners. Medical school usually provides ample opportunities to develop skills in working with peers in many projects starting with gross anatomy. The conditions of internship differ in that the amount of work is greater; the level of responsibility is profoundly different; and the relationships include a professional facet that is nearly absent from the relationships between students.

Students work together on laboratory teams, clinical teams, preparation of reports, and formal and informal study groups. Loyalty, dedication and group affiliation can run strongly in such groups, but ultimately the student is responsible mainly to his own standards. The individual intern represents the medical profession and bears heavy clinical and legal responsibility.

Interaction

While students expect of each other and usually provide consideration and cooperation, beginning with internship there is a sharp increase in expectations for professional dedication. Competence and devotion are usually present, but differences in style occur. These differences need to be learned and meshed to permit optimum functioning of the service. It is comparable to the process of integration that must take place when professional athletes join a team.

In professional athletics, subtleties of movement, feinting, timing and rhythm can become crucial. In a treatment team, methods of history taking, emphasis in reporting or note writing and strengths or deficiencies in development of differential diagnosis need to be taken into account. House officers differ in the diligence with which they pursue various treatment choices. Familiarity with these tendencies can affect patient care and the efficiency of performance of the clinical unit.

Interns tend to be more comfortable and productive if they can spend time together socially in pairs, in larger groups, and as a whole class. Parties, including spouses and lovers, tend to add opportunities for mutual acquaintance and understanding. Contacts among interns in and out of the hospital can enhance the likelihood that they will be able to understand each other's attitudes and styles and respond to them constructively and appropriately.

Temporary Disability

The impact of ordinary human occurrences like illness or injury tends to be magnified when they occur to interns. Most interns will try to continue working if their illnesses or injuries do not disable them, because they know that additional burdens will fall on their colleagues if they do not carry out their own work. Occasionally temporarily disabling illnesses and injuries occur, and this means that others in the internship class have to fill in by taking over clinical responsibilities. While this is usually accomplished with willingness, a sense of responsibility, and sympathy for the intern who is hurt, resentment is often felt if the illness or injury has been partly caused by the one who is sick or injured. This is similar to the feelings of resentment that arise toward patients who contribute to their own morbidity by smoking, overeating, taking drugs, or engaging in unnecessarily dangerous activities. In such situations, very often some members of the internship class feel sympathy for the intern who is ill or hurt, but others may also feel annoyance. This tends to divide the class, and may consequently reduce the collaborative, collegial atmosphere.

Pregnancy

Similar emotional responses may occur in relation to an intern who becomes pregnant. Pregnancy is very rarely viewed as a pure accident. While the right to bear children is usually defended by interns, the additional burdens of work imposed by maternity leave may be resented by female as well as male colleagues. Similar feelings of ambivalence may arise toward the milder complications of pregnancy if they impair the working ability of the pregnant intern.

An intern who is or who intends to become pregnant during PGY-1 can benefit by considering its effect on the class as well as on herself and her mate. Early disclosure to fellow interns and to the training director is likely to be most helpful to all concerned. Such revelation, if the pregnancy is not already obvious, can well be rehearsed mentally. Adverse reactions and comments by other physicians can be preprocessed through inner dialogue at any stage.

The mutual burdens imposed by the pregnant intern's temporary unavailability can best be assimilated by her colleagues if they can discuss the circumstances openly and early. It is particularly important that interns keep in mind the emotional issues as well as the effect on the working ability of the internship class as a whole. The integrity of that unit can be important to each of them as individuals and to the patients that they serve. The professional perspective can often be a helpful and unifying factor in such circumstances. The pregnant intern merits consideration and concern as a colleague, and perhaps as a friend. Unity in the internship class is also useful in the effort to obtain additional resources from the training program.

Most teaching hospitals and their specialty divisions and training directors have contingency plans for dealing with temporarily disabled interns. Since these usually involve some extra effort or expense, it is sometimes necessary that a unified request by the interns be made before such plans are activated.

Conflict Between Interns

The overwhelming majority of medical students and interns have healthy and well developed personalities. Sometimes, though, personalities may clash, and animosity may arise between two interns. The effectiveness and morale of both may suffer. Reverberations from these clashes may extend to the friends and sympathizers of one or both of the conflicting pair. When others are drawn in, morale problems may become more troublesome. Such conflicts are best resolved as quickly as possible.

If one or the other recognizes the possible impact of the conflict on professional responsibilities, then he may initiate an attempt to resolve their differences. Here again a professional outlook may help the individuals rise above their personal feelings of hurt, insult or discomfort. Open discussion between the two may result in successful resolution. If this does not work out, another intern may be invited to serve as a mediator. Other interns perceiving the conflict between their two colleagues may volunteer their services as unbiased third parties. While such offers may be perceived as intrusive in a personal relationship, the professional atmosphere may permit or even invite such mediation efforts.

If the conflict comes to the attention of residents or staff members, they may offer to serve as mediators. Another option is for them to request a consultation, a service that may be provided by the department of psychiatry.

Impairment

Impairment of an intern because of substance abuse, clinical depression, or even psychosis can be disturbing to the entire class. Individual offers of concern, help and consideration may sometimes be rejected. Assistance offered by other interns may not be sufficient. A problem then arises about obtaining additional help from the training program. Interns are often deeply troubled by the prospect of "blowing the whistle" on one of their colleagues. This may be felt by the impaired intern as a betrayal. The others may fear that revealing their colleague's psychiatric problem or substance abuse problem might ruin that person's career.

Usually the risk is far greater if the impairment results in harm to a patient. This could be a dreadful circumstance by itself and could certainly be a far greater factor in damaging the intern's future as a physician. A carefully and deliberately considered review of the possible consequences of reporting and of not reporting will likely lead to an intelligent and proper judgment. Sometimes consultation with a respected senior resident who can be trusted may help further. Usually there are faculty members who are not directly involved in the administration of the training program who can be relied upon to offer mature, detached consideration and information about how the administration handles such matters.

Such a trusted staff member may be approached with a request for confidentiality or with a request to consider a hypothetical situation. "What do you think ought to be done if we were to learn that one of the house officers has been abusing a drug and hasn't been at his best when he comes to work?"

Interns are usually astute and accurate in assessing the impairment of a colleague. If their careful, calm and good faith deliberations lead to the expectation that patient care may be compromised, then their professional duty, in my opinion, lies in insisting that the intern be evaluated properly by experts and that appropriate care be provided. In my view, there is a confluence of duties to patient, to the impaired intern, and to the profession. Many training programs are prepared to deal compassionately, effectively and constructively in helping to treat and restore interns suffering from such problems.

If such complicating events can be addressed and resolved, the internship group can be mutually supporting and rewarding. Long lasting and deeply meaningful friendships often arise during internship.

The gallows humor that interns share is fun. The brief respites from the burdens of work, the occasional triumphs, and the joy of learning can be shared and thereby magnified. Adversity experienced together can lead to an intimacy and to mutual regard that is hard to duplicate.

References

Blackwell B: Prevention of impairment among residents in training. JAMA 1986;255:1177-1178.

Borenstein DB, Cook K: Impairment prevention in the training years: A new mental health program at UCLA. JAMA 1982;247:2700-2703.

Borenstein DB: Availability of mental health resources for residents in academic medical centers. J Med Educ 1985;60:517-523.

Borenstein DB: Should physician training centers offer formal psychiatric assistance to house officers? A report on the major findings of a prototype program. Am J Psychiatry 1985;142:1053-1057.

Colford JM, McPhee SJ: The raveled sleeve of care: Managing the stresses of residency training. JAMA 1989;261:890-894.

Jellinek MS: Recognition and management of discord within house staff teams. JAMA 1986;256:754-755.

Jones EE: Interpreting interpersonal behavior: The effects of expectancies. Science 1986;234:41-46.

Lohr KM, Engbring NH: Institution-wide program for impaired residents at a major teaching hospital. J Medical Educ 1988;63:182-188.

Mellinkoff SM: The residency years. N Engl J Med 1989;320:1689-1690.

Miller JB: Toward a New Psychology of Women. Boston, Beacon Press, 1978.

Reynolds RE, Bice TW: Attitudes of medical interns toward patients and health professionals. J Health Soc Behav 1971;12:307-311.

Rosini L, Howell MC, Todres ID, et al: Group meetings in a pediatric intensive care unit. Pediatrics 1974;53:371-374.

Sheehan KH, Sheehan DV, White K, et al: A pilot study of medical student "abuse": Student perceptions of mistreatment and misconduct in medical school. JAMA 1990;263:533-537.

Siegel B, Donnelly JC: Enriching personal and professional development: The experience of a support group for interns. J Med Educ 1978;53:908-914.

Silver HK, Glicken AD: Medical student abuse: Incidence, severity and significance. JAMA 1990;263:527-532.

Small GW: House officer stress syndrome. Psychosomatics 1981;22:860-869.

Chapter 13

Learning From Others' Experience

Residents are the intern's teachers. They provide instruction, direction, information, leadership and reinforcement. These experienced house officers often provide personal guidance and assistance in coping with the stresses of internship in general and with the tasks of their specific unit in particular. They can acquaint interns with practical procedures. Having recently survived internship themselves, they are vital sources of suggestions about efficient ways to get things done. The tradition of residents teaching less experienced house officers is part of the basis for the close bond that commonly exists among physicians.

Casualties Among Elders

Unfortunately, some of these elders may themselves be casualties of the difficult postgraduate training experience. Perhaps the most common wound is antagonism toward patients. As mentioned earlier, and as many students themselves have observed, some residents and attending physicians appear hostile toward patients. Some of them have hardened the gallows humor that can be a comfort and a release for interns and residents into a somewhat malignant attitude. Making jokes about patients in the privacy of the house officers' on call rooms may siphon off part of the frustration, perhaps enough to enable them to work efficiently. Some carry the joking too far. After a while they get to believe the deprecating images about patients that appear in gallows humor and come to view the patients as nuisances, unworthy creatures, and all around burdens. These attitudes may crystallize into fairly fixed prejudices against patients, and malice and insensitivity may develop. Even when it only goes as far as frequent or constant deprecating humor about patients, a social ambience may be created that may erode the intern's idealism and compassion. It may also affect medical students on clinical rotation.

Junior residents (PGY-2) work under conditions not much easier than interns. They are on call frequently, and often have to work all night. They have the benefit of additional experience, knowledge and skill, since they have been at the process for one year more. Their physical exhaustion continues, however, as does the separation from family and the postponement of other sources of satisfaction. The longer the rigorous training continues, the greater the possibility that vitality, idealism and compassion may be eroded in some residents.

Much of what has been presented in this book about internship applies fairly closely to residency as well. Occasionally, residents will vent some of their own frustrations at interns who are subordinate to them.

Abusive Elders

A similar process affects a small but noticeable percentage of attending physicians whose personalities may have been twisted by the training process, and some whose personal behavior is difficult for other reasons. Interns are relatively defenseless in relation to such attending physicians in many institutions. The latter are known to embarrass and humiliate interns and sometimes even senior residents. Usually they rationalize their egotism and hostility as necessary for teaching or for discipline. They try to justify their nastiness under the rubric of some sort of aversive conditioning. Tantrums by a few surgeons in the operating room actually occur, as strange as that may seem to someone who has not witnessed such a performance. On hospital rounds, fits of ill temper by attendings of any of the specialties may be vented toward the house staff, but usually register a lower decibel level. This does not mean that they are any less regressed than ill-tempered surgeons but rather that they may be heard by visitors and others whom they are not able to intimidate.

Abusive behavior by senior residents or attending physicians can be painful, undermining and stressful. When such behavior is manifested by skillful and admired surgeons or knowledgeable and highly competent physicians, the effect on the intern can be disillusioning.

Coping With Abuse

Coping with such conduct, the intern can utilize some of the techniques described in the chapter on difficult behavior by patients. Directed fantasies, of both expressive and rehearsal types, can be employed. Consultation with one's peers can be helpful. Sometimes the intern can get advice from other residents on how best to deal with a rogue resident or attending physician.

The information gained from peers and from residents can help the intern to gain perspective and to understand the process. He can then probably manage to take it less personally and see it more as a problem in the senior person. At the same time, it is essential that the intern employ autognostic technics to ascertain his own contribution to the difficulty. Is there something that the intern does or omits that triggers or intensifies the harshness of the hostile attending?

Some interns may find that they are abused considerably more than their colleagues. If such a pattern is discerned, discovery of its mechanism is necessary to facilitate favorable change.

They may be victims of bigotry because of race, sex, ethnicity or other fairly obvious features. Others may fall into the idiosyncratic prejudices of individual senior people through behavior such as timidity, dependency, or indecisiveness. Traits such as confidence, boldness, meticulousness or a variety of others may attract the envy and enmity of people in the hierarchy who are not fully adapted to holding a position of power.

Some virtues when demonstrated to an unusual degree may arouse unfavorable responses. Examples are humility, courtesy or caution. It is difficult for some individuals to recognize that qualities that they prize about themselves may be resented by others. Friends, relatives or colleagues may be able to elucidate such problems.

The possibility must also be considered that the intern is provoking hostility. Traits not previously troublesome may intensify under stress. Irritability, arrogance or coldness may arise. A confidant can be helpful with recognition of such behavior if the intern inquires with an open mind.

Considered And Cautious Action

Any action taken by the intern in such circumstances, of course, is ultimately his own decision and responsibility. It is best that, before confronting the abusive elder, the intern discuss the situation with peers and with other residents. Vindictiveness is relatively rare in relationships between physicians, but it does occur. Action taken by interns with respect to attending physicians who are abusive, harassing or impaired, is best conducted by the intern class as a group. The chief resident should be informed, and his counsel sought. In less drastic situations where the misbehavior of the attending physician is confined to insults and other forms of verbal harassment, a critique by the internship class can sometimes be mutative.

Misbehavior of elders toward interns is relatively rare in most teaching hospitals. Considering such rarities can enable the student to rehearse responses well in advance. However, most of the time the elder physicians are like wise and caring older brothers and sisters.

References

Canavan DI: Prevention of impairment. J Med Soc NJ 1983;80:125-126.

Charach R, ed: The Naked Physician: Poems about the Lives of Patients and Doctors. Kingston, Ont, Quarry Press, 1990.

Coombs RH, May DS, Small GW, eds: Inside Doctoring: Stages and Outcomes in the Professional Development of Physicians. New York, Praeger, 1986.

Cousins N: Internship: Preparation or hazing? JAMA 1981;245:377.

Duffy JC: Emotional Issues in the Lives of Physicians. Springfield, IL, Charles C. Thomas, 1970.

Internship: Physicians Respond to Norman Cousins. JAMA 1981;246:2141-2144.

Jellinek MS: Recognition and management of discord within house staff teams. JAMA 1986;256:754-755.

Jensen PS: Barriers to working with impaired trainees: A resident's viewpoint. Psychiatr Q 1983;55:268-271.

Lang DA, Jara GB, Kessenick LW: The Disabled Physician: Problem Solving Strategies for the Medical Staff. Chicago, IL, American Hospital Publishing, Inc, 1989.

Lohr KM, Engbring NH: Institution-wide program for impaired residents at a major teaching hospital. J Medical Educ 1988;63:182-188.

McCue JD: The effects of stress on physicians and their medical practice. N Engl J Med 1982;306:458-463.

Mellinkoff SM: The residency years. N Engl J Med 1989;320:1689-1690.

Messner E: Inspiration of psychotherapists by patients. Am J Psychiatry 1976;133:1462-1463.

Pfifferling JH, Blum JC, Wood W: The prevention of physician impairment. J Fla Med Assoc 1981;68:268-273.

Reynolds RE, Bice TW: Attitudes of medical interns toward patients and health professionals. J Health Soc Behav 1971;12:307-311.

Rosenberg DA, Silver HK: Medical student abuse: An unnecessary and preventable cause of stress. JAMA 1984;251:739-742.

Rosini L, Howell MC, Todres ID, et al: Group meetings in a pediatric intensive care unit. Pediatrics 1974;53:371-374.

Sheehan KH, Sheehan DV, White K, et al: A pilot study of medical student "abuse": Student perceptions of mistreatment and misconduct in medical school. JAMA 1990;263:533-537.

Silver HK, Glicken AD: Medical student abuse: Incidence, severity and significance. JAMA 1990;263:527-532.

Small GW: House officer stress syndrome. Psychosomatics 1981;22:860-869.

Chapter 14

Relating To Other Hospital Personnel

Medical students on clinical rotations mainly work with house staff and, to a limited extent, with nurses. Students who serve a sub-internship or have had part time employment in a hospital will have worked with a variety of health professionals. Many students do not have much experience with social workers, technicians, ward secretaries, attendants, security personnel, administrators and other individuals employed in a hospital. Unless the student has a specific reason to think about them explicitly, these categories of hospital workers tend to be disregarded. Interns soon learn that people other than physicians occupy important positions in the comprehensive functioning of the hospital, even in patient care. Until the intern becomes acquainted with the significance of these other health workers and support personnel, relationships with them may proceed with a dissonant tone.

Wreckers and Fixers

A hierarchy exists in hospitals that is determined by education, experience, seniority, pay scale, and other factors. Many members of the system can interfere with its effective functioning more readily than even the most dedicated can contribute to its improvement. Wrecking is easier than fixing. Ill feeling, engendered in some of the people with whom he must work, can add to the intern's burdens. If a nurse, a ward secretary or an attendant responds to the intern's request with enthusiasm, or with reluctance or delay, the difference in effect can be substantial. The functions that the various hospital employees serve can be readily appreciated by the intern, and if he shows them reasonable respect, it is likely that he will meet with greater cooperation.

Hospital workers are notoriously poorly paid. It is not only the interns or residents who are underpaid in relation to their knowledge and skill. Many people who choose employment in hospitals do so in part because of the satisfaction that they get from being contributors to the care of the sick. If the intern recognizes those contributions through his demeanor and communications, he will find himself leading a more smoothly functioning clinical team.

Recognition Of Individuality

Another feature that can further enhance the effectiveness of the intern's work is developing an acquaintance with the other hospital workers as individuals. As mentioned above, respect for their function is important. Recognition of the individual performer can intensify the sense of collaboration. This does not necessarily mean extensive personal interaction. Even a brief recognition of an individual feature in a hospital worker's life, such as family composition or recreational interest, can prove to be gratifying to both. It can not only improve collaboration, but in most instances, can make the work experience a bit more human and less austere than it might be otherwise.

Excessive Intimacy

Problems may arise at the other end of the spectrum. Just as disrespect or aloofness can provoke conflict or passive aggressive behavior, so can excessive intimacy engender its share of problems. The greatest of these problems arise in regard to the social, emotional and sexual deprivation that interns often suffer. Interns who are unmarried may suffer loneliness and hunger for companionship. At the same time, the exhausting work schedule prevents them from engaging in the usual activities that bring young people together. In the hospital a large number of interested, attractive and available young people are encountered in day-to-day work. Temptations to develop personal relationships are considerable.

Interns sometimes become socially or sexually interested in other house officers. Most of the difficulties that arise in hospital romances apply to those between two physicians just about as much as they do to those between physicians and others.

Interns who are married, or who are living in an intimate relationship, may also be tempted to enter a romantic relationship with someone at the hospital. If they are encountering distress at home, it can be enticing to look elsewhere for comfort, understanding and sympathy. Intimacy with attractive and interested young people with whom the intern is not experiencing intense conflict can be difficult to resist.

Moral and ethical considerations apply here. Though they may be swept aside by passion, they have ways of asserting themselves belatedly and sometimes as disguised self-punishment. This is in addition to the hazards of sexually transmitted diseases.

Romantic relationships with people in the work place, such as the hospital, can impair working relationships. They can destabilize functional units by arousing feelings of jealousy, competition, rejection and embarrassment. If the relationship founders, it can leave two people with hostility, disappointment or embitterment toward each other, but who are required to work together on a day-to-day basis. These problems are relatively small compared to the problems of misjudgment that may emerge when marriages develop out of a situation of intense personal stress.

Crisis-Driven Overinvolvement

It is fairly common knowledge that it is risky to enter into a serious relationship immediately after one has recently ended, whether through estrangement, rejection, divorce or widowhood. Such rebound relationships can be dangerous because they are based upon the gratification of intense immediate needs and the torments of loneliness, disruption and grief. Relationships originating in a crisis may not have lasting qualities.

In situations of intense and desperate emotional need, like those experienced by interns, long-term prospects may be ignored. If consequences are considered at all, they may be rationalized or distorted to suit the circumstances of the moment. If one is to enter into something like a marital relationship, it is crucial to be able to think ahead and consider what will this relationship be like five years hence, or ten years, or longer. Sometimes these relationships are established on the basis of satisfaction of immediate and intense feelings of isolation or deprivation. The two participants may not have compatible interests, attitudes, qualities, values or aspirations that could form the basis for a lasting relationship. The result may be something that will lead to strife, separation or divorce after the conditions of immediate need are ended.

Many divorces occur not too long after physicians complete their residency training. The spouse who supported the physician through his arduous training both financially and emotionally, may feel bitter and cheated. Both may recognize their incompatibility as individuals in a circumstance that does not involve the demands and separations of training. If there are children, the situation becomes increasingly complex, difficult and painful. Serious and lasting problems may be inflicted upon the children.

Hasty overinvolvement can be prevented in the case of the intern, despite his depletion or personal turmoil. It is hazardous to make decisions that can have a lasting and profound effect on one's life, or the life of someone important, if those decisions are made under conditions of emotional duress.

By recognizing and reflecting upon these circumstances and opportunities, the intern may be able to prevent disastrous involvement or disruption of his existing spousal relationship. He can confide in friends, colleagues, family, experienced physicians, professional counselors or therapists.

Interns who have not prepared themselves for the personal stresses of postgraduate training may not even recognize the intensity of their needs or the desperation of their impulses. They may involve themselves deeply in relationships without clearly recognizing some of their motivations or the possible consequences of what they are doing. All of this may occur rapidly and impulsively, even in individuals who are otherwise thoughtful and deliberate. Anticipation of these circumstances can enable the student to be prepared, and perhaps prevent himself from falling victim to his own very human needs.

References

Asken MJ, Raham DC: Resident performance and sleep deprivation: A review. J Med Ed 1983;58:382-388.

Bates EM, Moore BN: Stress in hospital personnel. Med J Aust 1975;2:765-767.

Goldman JD: An elective seminar to teach first-year students the social and medical aspects of AIDS. J Med Educ 1987;62:557-561.

Jones EE: Interpreting interpersonal behavior: The effects of expectancies. Science 1986;234:41-46.

Matthews DA, Classen DC, Willms JL, et al: A program to help interns cope with stresses in an internal medicine residency. J Med Educ 1988;63:539-547.

Miller JB: Toward a New Psychology of Women. Boston, Beacon Press, 1978.

Schluger N: Residents' work schedules. JAMA 1989;261:3548-3549.

Stein S: The House of God. New York, Dell, 1978.

Vaillant GE, Sobowale NC, McArthur C: Some psychologic vulnerabilities of physicians. N Engl J Med 1972;287:372-375.

Chapter 15

Unplanned Personally Demanding Events

Involvement in an intimate relationship is largely a matter of personal decision, although feelings can be aroused spontaneously and reach an intense amplitude. Actions in response to such emotions are matters of choice. The individual has control over what he does, even if there seems to be no way to reduce the intensity of emotion.

Ordinary life presents numerous events that can be personally demanding, but over which the individual has no control. Illnesses, injuries, death or other personal disasters can occur to people who are important to interns just as they can occur to anyone else. If the intern, members of his family or even his colleagues become disabled, emotional and practical demands will ensue. Misfortune can assail anyone, but when it occurs in an intern's life, consequences can be especially troublesome. Since the intern is already functioning at maximum capacity in most instances, there is little or no reserve for dealing with additional burdens.

Anticipating Trouble

Although such events cannot be planned and are outside the control of the intern, they can, in a general sense, be anticipated. This projection into the future is similar to the kind discussed in the chapter on mental rehearsal. If the student thinks ahead about the people who are most important to him and toward whom he feels responsibility or duty — parents, siblings, other relatives, friends, spouse, his own offspring — he can consider what might happen and what his response may be. This may be perceived as a gloomy and morbid mental exercise. The distressing quality of it may be partly compensated by the recognition that such anticipation may enable the intern to respond more effectively and more humanely.

Preparation and Prevention

Another effect is that it may direct the student toward preventive preparations that can be practical and compassionate. Such a mental review may remind the student that he has not kept current with important events in the lives of those who are emotionally close to him. It may lead to more contact with the lives of those who are dear. This may contribute to a greater ability to predict what might happen, but it can also serve as an opportunity to demonstrate caring and concern. It can revive personal ties, and fortify the emotional lives of the student and of those who are his greatest concern.

A review of this sort can lead to practical ways of making things better, perhaps helping to prevent some of the personal catastrophes that can be imagined. A grandparent living alone may be suffering from progressive arthritis without adequate physical therapy, occupational therapy and home health care. All of that could be arranged to help maintain the elderly person's independence and dignity. The student's mother may be neglecting her hypertension or diabetes. A younger brother may be experimenting with illegal drugs. Appropriate attention from the student might arrest progression of such problems.

Practical matters may require attention. The student's widowed mother may not be arranging for repairs or maintenance for her house. Wills and insurance may have been neglected.

Enhanced communication can also provide the student with a clear idea of what additional assistance can be called upon. Are there other family members who could help in a crisis? Are there friends? Are there other resources? Discussion of possible difficulties can lead to a clarification of the degree of responsibility or division of duties that may be relevant and appropriate. Such discussion among family members and others, enriched with compassion and consideration, can preempt conflict and reduce recrimination and guilt should a catastrophic event occur.

Practical Matters

Academic demands on the medical student added to the efforts required to finance his education leave little energy for attention to practical matters in the lives of others. We physicians

122

have reputations for being relatively naive and gullible about money and investments. In part this may relate to academic preoccupations during years that most people are more focused on material concerns.

Regardless of his personal inclinations or experience, the intern will be drawn into consideration of the practical circumstances of his patients' lives. Matters of health insurance, availability of nursing care after discharge from the hospital, arrangements for obtaining medications and for transportation to follow-up clinic appointments, and numerous other factors will influence the outcome of hospital treatment. Effective case management requires understanding such matters and many more.

Social service departments in teaching hospitals provide experts for implementation of after-care plans. The intern must understand enough to make a referral and to be able to intervene when problems arise.

Eventually, most interns become knowledgeable and skillful in supervising these arrangements. Their patients benefit as a result. Often similar problems confront their own relatives. The student or intern may be unaware of their present or future needs or how he might be helpful.

Discovering the practical needs and possibilities among his loved ones can show him how meaningful they can be. That in turn can help him understand more deeply the comparable predicaments among his patients. This experience with his own family can help him become a more complete physician.

The chapter on preparing family and friends focused on the altered circumstances that the student will enter when internship begins. This is a comparable preparation, with family, friends and other important people, for crises that might arise, and how each, including the intern, will help cope with them.

Estrangement, Separation and Bereavement

Disruption of a relationship with a spouse or lover can be devastatingly disturbing to anyone. Under the stresses of internship impairment of an intimate relationship can be destabilizing.

One of the risks of developing an intimate relationship is the possibility of loss. It is the fear of such loss that sometimes prevents people from commitment to a relationship of love and devotion. The circumstances of internship clearly impose considerable stress on a romantic relationship, and its deterioration or dissolution is something that needs to be considered.

Preparation of the interns' mate, as described in an earlier chapter (#8), can help fortify the relationship. It may help to preserve the dyad throughout the difficult training period. Despite such preparation, relationships may experience considerable strain and may crack as a result.

In addition to the separations that are imposed by the intern's duties, numerous other factors can disrupt intimacy. These include all of the difficulties that can occur even under less stressful work conditions: incompatibility, disillusionment, attraction to other people, intrusions of various kinds. Those ordinary factors, added to the stressfulness of house officer training, can undermine the relationship.

Estrangement may occur emotionally, even though the couple may continue to live together or to maintain their usual contacts. The possibility of separation, of course, will exist as long as conflict and disaffection present a serious threat.

A couple can be parted by other factors. The intern's mate may be required to move elsewhere because of requirements of his or her employment. There may be professional or educational demands or opportunities that cannot be resisted without major sacrifice. This may lead to a geographic separation that may erode the attachment.

Although a less frequent occurrence in people of house officer age, the intern's lover may die as a result of illness or accident. This is an irreversible loss difficult to contemplate by people who love each other.

Coping With Loss Of An Intimate Relationship

An event of this magnitude requires employment of the maximum effectiveness of the intern's coping skills. He needs to review his experience with losses in the past to sort out which adaptive methods were effective, and which were undermining. If there seems to be no precedent for such a personal loss in the intern's history, he may review other experiences: losses of friends, separations, losses of function at times when he may have been injured. There may have been losses resulting from geographic separations as when he left home for college or moved to another city or medical school. Even though such separations were relatively mild, were expectable, and in some instances even part of a desired progress in his personal development, his behavior at such junctures may give some hint regarding the most effective way to cope with the poignant loss of a lover.

In addition to a review of his own experience with estrangement and bereavement, it is advisable for the affected individual to review all of the methods suggested in the previous chapters as a kind of check list. It might enable him to find sustenance and relief under these especially difficult circumstances.

Even in a situation in which the intern himself initiates the disruption of the relationship, difficulties may ensue. Some people find that rejecting is less threatening and disturbing than being rejected. For that reason, they may end the relationship or provoke an interruption in order to feel the relative comfort of being in some control of the situation. Even in such circumstances, the eventual disruption can affect the initiator with surprisingly intense self-blame.

Intimate relationships are treasured human experiences. They deserve the cultivation and hard work that will enable them to persist and succeed. Bereavement, of course, can usually not be prevented. It is essential for the intern's stability or functional survival that the impact of loss of such a relationship not be underestimated.

References

Aoun H: When a house officer gets AIDS. N Eng J Med 1989;321:693-696.

Duffy JC: Emotional Issues in the Lives of Physicians. Springfield, IL, Charles C. Thomas, 1970.

Mazie B: Job stress, psychological health and social supports of family practice residents. J Med Educ 1985;60:935-941.

Nelson FG, Henry WF: Psychosocial factors seen as problems by family practice residents and their spouses. J Fam Pract 1978;6:581-589.

Pekkanen J: Doctors Talk About Themselves. New York, Delacorte Press, 1988.

Pepitone-Arreola-Rockwell F, Rockwell D, Core N: Fifty-two medical student suicides. Am J Psychiatry 1981;138:198-201.

Reuben DB: Psychologic effects of residency. Southern Med J 1983; 76:380-383.

Sheehy G: Passages: Predictable Crises of Adult Life. New York, Dutton, 1976.

Silver RL, Wortzman CB: Coping with undesirable life events. In Garber J, Seligman MEP, eds: Human Helplessness. New York, Academic Press 1980:279-340.

Tokarz JP, Bremer W, Peter K: Beyond Survival. Chicago, AMA 1979.

Zabarenko R, Zabarenko L: The Doctor Tree: Development Stages in the Growth of Physicians. Pittsburgh, University of Pittsburgh Press, 1978.

Chapter 16

Hospital Bureaucracy And Ethical Dilemmas

Medical students enter the teaching hospital focused on learning medicine and surgery directly with patients. Their interest is excited by the professional, medical, educational aspects of their work, and they tend to pay little attention to organizational factors. Certainly they need to learn to find the department office and the clinical units to which they are assigned. They may become acquainted with the secretary in the training director's office, but primarily they are interested in the patients, interns, residents and teaching physicians. The student is interested in learning medical and surgical procedures not bureaucratic procedures.

The object of the intern's interest remains essentially the same: learning and practicing the care of patients. But the intern immediately becomes a unit of a complex system that has its own rules and procedures. After twelve or more years of school, and then college and medical school, the student is already aware of some of the complexities that bureaucracies can impose. The purpose of this chapter is to call attention to some of the specific ways that organizational procedures, forms and other kinds of red tape can affect the intern's already complicated activities. Once again, this is in the interest of preparation and mental rehearsal.

Many teaching hospitals provide interns with printed copies of the procedures that must be followed in writing orders, completing charts, requesting consultations, communicating with referring physicians, and other activities that are closely related to patient care. While the intern is probably most interested in the procedures to be followed in a code or in preparing a patient for major surgery, the others will become a daily part of his life. Some of the procedures will probably make good sense; and others will probably be cumbersome, time consuming, and inefficient. A few will be quaint reminders of the nineteenth century. Many will change with each new federal effort to pay for its waste, corruption and imprudence at the expense of the ill, the injured and the infirm.

Some teaching hospitals send packets of such information to interns in advance of the training year. Others also provide orientation sessions prior to the beginning of the training year.

Many will not provide any advance orientation but will impose a great sheaf of papers, forms, and brochures along with several hours of orientation on the first day when the intern is desperately trying to learn his initial clinical duties.

It is obviously very tempting to set aside these bureaucratic procedures in the interest of getting directly at the clinical ones. Organizational red tape and forms, and even some of the administrators themselves, become ready targets for the frustration and resentment that overburdened interns often feel. Difficulties arise for interns when their resentment interferes with their willingness to learn the procedures.

That sort of passive rebellion can be counterproductive. This is not to say that all procedures, however foolish and inefficient, should be supinely accepted by the intern, but if he is not clear about how to get things done as decreed by his hospital's administrators, the intern is going to add to his own load of work. The more effective strategy is usually to learn how things get done in the hospital and to get advice from more experienced residents about how best to carry out his duties. Some of the ward clerks or department secretaries can be extremely helpful in some matters, and their knowledge and good will can often be easily cultivated.

Coping With Bureaucracy

There may be regulations, forms and practices in a hospital that desperately need to be changed. This sort of problem is best approached with careful thought, with a consensus of interns and residents, and, if possible, with the support of the training director and the chief of service. Sometimes hospital administrations unilaterally change the rules in the middle of the game: withhold promised salary increases, increase service requirements, or decrease teaching, electives or some of the other benefits given to house staff. Shortages of medications or equipment, matters that are of tremendous direct clinical importance may also develop. When such circumstances arise, political action may be necessary, but this is best accomplished with detailed, concerted preparation and not as an impulsive result of outrage. It is especially important to refrain from using the organizational aspect of internship as a displaced outlet for pent up hostilities arising from other aspects of the intern's life.

Procedures like rehearsal fantasies, conversations with peers, gallows humor, and others can be well applied to the organization burdens. The intern has too little available energy to squander it unnecessarily on conflicts that may not be worth the effort and may not be winnable.

Ethical Dilemmas and Limited Resources

This is an important consideration because some extremely urgent and potent conflicts can arise in the area of ethical choices that the intern will be forced to make. Any system has finite resources. Teaching hospitals often reach their limits of ability to admit patients or to care for a large number of casualties who are brought in simultaneously. Beds may not be available. There may be a limit imposed on how many indigent patients can be treated. The blood bank contains only a limited number of units. The intern very often will be the one who must choose which patient will get treatment and which will not, which patient will be admitted and which will not.

The limited resources include the time and energy of the available house staff. The intern may be faced with requirements to care for the patient with AIDS who has been taking drugs intravenously, or an infant who has AIDS acquired at birth. Intense feelings are bound to arise, especially in relation to patients who have somehow contributed to their own disease. The intern might be faced with providing transfusions for someone who has developed esophageal hemorrhage as a result of alcohol abuse, when that same blood might be needed for a child who was injured in an automobile accident.

Some choices are imposed by limits of available resources. Other choices are imposed by administrative rules. When care of patients is obstructed by financial considerations such as lack of health insurance, the emotional impact on the intern is usually powerful, not to mention the suffering, morbidity, or death of the neglected patient. It is in these situations in which patient care is sabotaged as a result of organizational strictures that feelings of frustration and resentment are most intense.

Clinical Benefits of Bureaucratic Skill

These are circumstances in which expert knowledge of the hospital's bureaucratic procedures may result in benefit to patients. Knowing which officials are able to get things done, are willing to stretch the rules, and can recruit help from other parts of the health care system may enable the intern to obtain more for his patients. Skillful influence of the system by the intern can be legal, moral and honorable. It can be another way that the intern can provide the best for his patients that his hospital – and the health care network of the city, county and state – can muster.

It requires learning more about the rules rather than rejecting them with hostility. Interns who learn to play this high stakes game successfully may even derive some satisfaction from it, but even they may at times be tempted to rebel.

Before acting on an impulse to defy the rules, it is important for the intern to think through the consequences of doing it and of not doing it. Consulting a trusted senior can be valuable. It is essential to emphasize the distinction between action and vocalizing a protest. The consequences differ. One can object vehemently to a set of rules, particularly those that affect patients severely, but remain under duress to follow them. Sometimes disobedient behavior is the best, most moral and medically correct course. Such considerations are brought to the student's attention here so that they can be thought through in advance. The specifics will have to be considered when the actual circumstance arises.

Impulsive action can be unprofessional and may be detrimental to the very patients that the intern is concerned about. It may further deplete the intern's limited stores of energy and in that way secondarily harm patients. If these matters are considered in advance, rehearsed mentally, and discussed with friends and mentors, the chances of making sound, appropriate and effective judgments are increased substantially.

References:

Arras JD. The fragile web of responsibility: AIDS and the duty to treat. Hastings Center Rep 1988;18(2):Suppl:10-20.

Beauchamp T, Childress JF: Ideals, virtues and conscientious actions, in principles of Biomedical Ethics. New York, Oxford University Press, 1983.

Bronner E: The foot soldiers of medicine. The Boston Sunday Globe Magazine, July 6, 1986.

Culver CM, Clouser KD, Gert B, et al: Basic curricular goals in medical ethics. N Engl J Med 1985;312:253-256.

Drane JF: Becoming a Good Doctor: The Place of Virtue and Character in Medical Ethics. Kansas City, MO, Sheed and Ward, 1988.

Hilfiker D: Allowing the debilitated to die: Facing our ethical choices. N Engl J Med 1983;308:716-719.

Kay J: Traumatic deidealization and the future of medicine. JAMA 1990;263:572-573.

Luce JM: Ethical principles in critical care. JAMA 1990;263:696-700.

McCall TB: No turning back: A blueprint for residency reform. JAMA 1989;261:909-910.

McCall TB: Residents' work schedules: In reply. JAMA 1989;261:3549.

Novack DH, Detering BJ, Arnold R, et al: Physicians; attitudes toward using deception to resolve difficult ethical problems. JAMA 1989;261:2980-2985.

Schluger N: Residents' work schedules. JAMA 1989;261:3548-3549.

Shapiro E, Lowenstein L, eds: Becoming a Physician: Development of Values and Attitudes in Medicine. Cambridge, MA, Allinger, 1979.

Stein S: The House of God. New York, Dell, 1978.

Winkenwerder W: Ethical dilemmas for house staff physicians: The care of critically ill and dying patients. JAMA 1985;254:3454-3457.

Chapter 17

Major Personal Decisions

Interns make innumerable decisions, some of which have enormous impact on their patients. Clinical decisions and treatment interventions can be matters of death or survival for patients. They also make day-to-day choices affecting their own lives and futures.

The period of house officer training is one in which the young physician selects among highly significant alternatives regarding his further training and his career. In addition, during the years of the late twenties and early thirties the house officer may be involved in establishing important intimate relationships and perhaps starting a family. Elections to enter a medical or surgical specialty, or to change from one specialty to another are clearly important and will affect the individual for some time, perhaps for his entire career. Similarly, decisions to separate or to divorce will have enormous effect on his future for years, perhaps for life.

For anyone, choices of such magnitude deserve careful deliberation and thought. For the intern, in particular, careful reasoning and objectivity need to be introduced because the intern will be exercising these options under conditions of considerable stress. Choices made under pressure are fraught with a greater possibility of error or misjudgment than comparable choices made in conditions of tranquility.

The process of decision making can be organized in various ways. Objectivity is an essential factor in clinical reasoning. An equivalent level of detachment may not be attainable in the personal realm. Important choices made haphazardly or at a moment of emotional intensity can be exciting and romantic but can also be disadvantageous or potentially harmful. This is not to say that the inspiration and creativity that the intern may possess should be ignored.

Goals

Choices serve multiple motivations. They seek goals and avoidance of perceived trouble. It is important that the person who is making the decision consider explicitly his expectations, ideals and hopes with respect to the proposed choice.

Many students incur large debts to pay for their schooling. As a result many choose highly renumerative surgical specialties or medical specialties with well paid invasive procedures. These highly technical diagnostic and therapeutic methods are usually commensurately valuable in patient care. They are also exciting and challenging. There is much to recommend them.

However, they may not permit the long term relationships with patients found in primary care specialties. An intern who seeks to treat patients and their families over time might become dissatisfied with a procedure oriented practice.

Avoidances

It is important to review what is being avoided, if anything, by making the choice under consideration. An intern who values direct contact with patients may enter pathology or laboratory research because he dreads malpractice litigation. Since pathology and research are valuable, challenging and rewarding pursuits, the student may rationalize his choice. He may suppress, forget or ignore his concerns about lawsuits.

Later on he might experience significant dissatisfaction at the absence of direct patient care. Such an outcome may be prevented by confronting and overcoming the forensic fears.

Conversely, a talented and enthusiastic potential laboratory scientist might avoid committing himself to research because he fears he might be insufficiently productive. If confronted directly, that fear might be overcome. Or the intern might then come to grips with his inner demands for productivity. Are they realistic? Are they insatiable? What are his standards and on what are they based?

In addition to the primary goals or avoidances, there may be secondary consequences to the decision. An example is that moving to another city for a particularly desirable fellowship will mean parting with friends.

Antecedents

In analyzing a decision, it can be particularly instructive to think through its antecedents. Are there any precedents in the intern's life: comparable decisions? How did they work out in the past? With what method were comparable choices made previously? How did they fare? Are the choices, in fact, based upon current and future considerations or are major determinants based in his history? Did the intern decide to go into a subspecialty of internal medicine because this is something that his father yearned for but was unable to accomplish? Is the intern fulfilling someone else's dream and thinking of it as his own? The choice may still be a proper one, but recognition of those other influences can be helpful and perhaps enriching.

Alternatives

In making choices, it is of course important to consider the alternatives. What else is available, and what is the comparable value of the alternatives? What might be the goals or consequences or origins?

Gathering Data

In preparing for a major choice very often additional information is needed. This may become evident as the process proceeds. In making a decision about further training, of course, it is clear that investigation of all aspects of the training program is appropriate.

Although this may seem unromantic, decisions about marriage or having children also require a great deal of information, thought, discussion and contemplation. Factual information and the process of collecting it can add objectivity. Family histories of neurologic or hematologic disorders should be known, if possible, before marriage or before conception rather than afterward. But many ordinary human issues need to be discussed and understood in detail. Couples are wise to discuss their respective attitudes about size of families, religious devotion, contacts with their own parents and other family members, and about material circumstances. Most religions provide helpful pre-marital counseling. For those people without religious affiliation, outlines or models for such mutual discussion can be found in books and can be sought from respected friends and relatives who have had successful marriages. Those who have been separated or divorced should not be ignored in this regard. Often they have learned very painfully from their experience and can be extremely helpful in offering caution and suggestions to others.

Review And Consultation

All of the foregoing factors can be reviewed with inner dialogue or in discussions with other people. These others may be confidants or experts, as the situation may direct.

Contingencies need to be considered. What can go wrong, and if it goes wrong, what can be done about it?

Pathology teaches us that every phase of embryological development, feature of anatomy, physiological process or biochemical reaction can go awry in one or more ways. Comparable complexity pervades the procedures of diagnosis and management in medicine, surgery, and their specialties. This is part of the fascination and challenge of our profession.

Our training directs us to anticipate complications and adverse reactions by preparing to recognize and to respond to them constructively. To a large extent we can apply similar analytical thinking and planning to personal situations.

Some may object that such rationality can spoil the fun and suppress initiative. This need not happen. To extend the professional parallel, some of the most optimistic and effective surgeons are those who are familiar with the hazards of their craft and are prepared to overcome adverse responses. The most determinedly persistent physicians are often those who anticipate and are thus more able to resolve complications.

Analysis and deliberation can improve the likelihood of favorable outcome. They can also focus attention on the richness, complexity and variety of adult life.

Other elements belong to the organization of the decision making process. Considerations of timing, of resources necessary for implementation of a decision, and of the cooperation of other people are factors that need to be taken into account. Options can be evaluated in terms of benefit and cost, or benefit and risk. (see Table 17.1).

Students or interns who are accustomed to acting spontaneously or intuitively may find an organized procedure burdensome and tedious. Where major personal decisions with lasting effect are concerned, whimsy, spontaneity and verve need not be disregarded. They are, in fact, precious ingredients of creativity that deserve to be treasured and cultivated. They need not always be acted upon, but employment of a systematic approach to decision making may well reinforce the products of intuition. At the same time, bringing to bear the cognitive and objective factors that were noted above can add some assurance to their validity, appropriateness and durability.

References

Coombs RH, May DS, Small GW, eds: Inside Doctoring: Stages and Outcomes in the Professional Development of Physicians. New York, Praeger, 1986.

Coste C: The risky business of becoming a doctor. New Physician 1978;27:28-31.

Erikson EH: Identify and the Life Cycle. Psychological Issues 1959;1(1):1-171. New York, International Universities Press.

Kohner M: Becoming a Doctor: A Journey of Initiation in Medical School. New York, Penguin Books, 1988.

Kris K: Developmental strains of women medical students. J Am Med Wom Assoc 1985;40:145-148,

McCue JD: The effects of stress on physicians and their medical practice. N Engl J Med 1982;306:458-463.

Pekkanen J: Doctors Talk About Themselves. New York, Delacorte Press, 1988.

Sharaf M, Levinson D: The quest for omnipotence in professional training. Int J Psychiatry 1967;4:426-454.

Sheehy G: Passages: Predictable Crises of Adult Life. New York, Dutton, 1976.

Stein HF: The Psychodynamics of Medical Practice. Berkeley, University of California Press, 1985.

Tokarz JP, Bremer W, Peters K: Beyond Survival. Chicago, AMA 1979.

Zabarenko R, Zabarenko L: The Doctor Tree: Development Stages in the Growth of Physicians. Pittsburgh, University of Pittsburgh Press, 1978.

TABLE 17.1 – **Considerations in Major Decisions**

—*Function*
- Goals
  - Expectations
  - Ideals
- Avoidances
  - Aversions
  - Fears

—*Antecedents*

—*Consequences*

—*Alternatives*

—*Research*

—*Review and consultation*
- Inner dialogue
- Outer dialogue with
  - Confidants
  - Experts

—*Contingencies*

—*Other Factors*
- Timing
- Resources required
  - Physical and material
  - Financial
  - Human

—*Anticipatory evaluations*
- Benefits
- Costs
- Risks

Chapter 18

Adding Insights from Associative Introspection

Spontaneous associations can arise as emotions, fantasies, images, impulses, remembered dreams or thoughts that may float into one's consciousness. They usually do not follow the rules of logic that we are trained to follow from early childhood. Since they tend to remain outside the realm of the usual conscious thinking that is rational and purposeful, they tend to be set aside, suppressed or ignored.

Special attention is required by most people to notice spontaneous associations. They can be observed in the gaps between the logical thoughts that we try to communicate to each other, or they may drift around the thinking that is usually employed for problem solving. When a memory seems to pop into consciousness, or an image arises in one's mind, it may be perceived as an extraneous nuisance.

Free Associations

Near the end of the nineteenth century, two Viennese physicians, Josef Breuer and Sigmund Freud, observed that such mental products, which they called "free associations," could be useful. They could help lead to an understanding of aspects of personal development and elucidate various emotional disorders. Freud, and psychoanalysts who followed him, employed the observation of free associations as central data in psychoanalysis. Patients who are treated psychoanalytically or with a modification, psychoanalytic psychotherapy, often become skillful in perceiving and using their own free associations. Many people are capable of observing these spontaneous mental productions even without such therapy.

Spontaneous Associations

As psychoanalysts have observed for nearly one hundred years, attention to spontaneous associations can add greatly to understanding human beings and their experiences. If a resident recognizes the potential value of such observations in understanding himself, he has taken the first step toward using them for added autognosis. In fact, it is not even necessary to believe that observing these spontaneous fantasies and other associations is useful. One needs merely to recognize that mental experiences other than simple logical thought arise in consciousness, and one can decide to observe them and to see how they evolve, connect, merge into one another, and interplay with one's emotions and attitudes.

An attitude of receptivity and willingness to observe is all that is needed. Even someone skeptical of the potential value of such observations can allow himself a special experience with his own inner functioning: contemplation of the fantasies and imagery that are usually ignored or subordinated to logical thought. This may lead to deeper understanding, to new ways of observing, and to new questions about experience. Scanning spontaneous associations may lead to expansion of awareness of one's strivings and fears. It may bring about new perspectives on other people and on events outside one's self.

Directed Associations

Directed association is a more active, organized and goal oriented variant of the associative method. It starts with a personal experience such as a painful feeling, a fantasy, a symptom such as insomnia, a set of fearsome images or dream material. It utilizes internal dialogue. One takes the experience and asks what comes to mind in association to this experience. One then tries to take note of the thoughts, impulses, feelings or memories that may float to consciousness subsequent to this internal question. What comes up may not seem to bear a logical connection with the starting point. That is one of the intriguing yet complicating features of associative processes. They may not connect in terms of ordinary day-to-day logic, but it is best to take note of those emerging experiences. They can include the entire spectrum of inner perceptions, including memories of music, images, or bits of song lyrics; they may be people or emotions from the past.

The process may be complicated even further by the intrusion of other thoughts or perceptions of current experience or problems. Thoughts about the task at hand, or recent experience, or unfinished work may come up to interrupt the chain of associations. When that happens, or when the process seems to stall for any reason, one may push it ahead by asking once again what comes to mind, but this question may be directed toward the most recent or the most prominent association. For example, if the stream of associations leads to the memory of a person one has known, a program seen on television, or a dream, those can be employed as the starting points for the next segment of the associative sequence.

The objects of this quest may include disquieting feelings. They may lead toward experiences that were painful or that might become painful again. They may lead toward ideas about which one may feel ashamed. The discovery may be one that is useful but at the same time may have some distressing awareness involved. Such disclosures are defended against spontaneously. As hard as one might try to uncover the truth, one's own mind may try to protect its relative comfort by erecting obstacles or actively opposing the process. This opposition, or resistance, may take the form of tiredness, a sense of futility, an idea that "This isn't leading anywhere", or "It's a waste of time", or just a temporary blankness of mind. The last is quite a rare experience. Instead of blankness, very often one's mind might be pre-empted by more usual conscious day-to-day thoughts and feelings. Sometimes one can break the inner log jam by going back to an earlier association and starting fresh. Other times it is necessary to allow the mental tangle to loosen up by setting it aside temporarily and returning to it on another occasion.

A more active way of working out a resistance may be to ask oneself, "What am I afraid of discovering?" Or one may associate to

"This isn't leading anywhere."
"This is a waste of time."

Observation of the ensuing fantasies may be of some help. This procedure employs associations to the resistance in a manner comparable to associations to the primary content.

Despite sincere effort and perseverance, associative introspection may not lead to resolution of the problem or relief of the symptom that the intern is suffering. If this effort does not suffice, and other efforts at problem solving and adaptation have not led to resolution of the problem, then the intern needs to contemplate obtaining professional consultation. The intern is duty-bound to prevent his own difficulties from interfering with patient care. His own suffering and impairment of aspects of his personal functioning equally deserve serious consideration.

Apart from therapy, artists, poets, musicians, and other creative people employ these mental experiences. Spontaneously evolving images, memories and ideas can be experienced by anyone as one might respond to poetry, abstract painting, or classical music.

Many who observe the spontaneous productions of their own minds delight in their complexity, generativity and beauty. Such mental experiences are probably present in most, if not all, human beings. By contemplating what floats to consciousness one may be comforted by its intricacy. It can arouse wonderment akin to that of children looking closely at the veins of a leaf, the patterns of snowflakes or at the rich and colorful evolution of clouds in a sunset. This too can help sustain the intern.

References:

Freud S: An outline of psychoanalysis. in The Complete Psychological Works of Sigmund Freud, Vol XXIII. London, Hogarth Press, 1974.

Gottschalk LA: How to Do Self-Analysis and Other Self Psychotherapies. Northvale, NJ, Jason Aronson, 1989.

Greenson R: The Technique and Practice of Psychoanalysis. New York, International Universities Press, 1967.

Hendrick I: Facts and Theories of Psychoanalysis. New York, Alfred A. Knopf, 1958.

Chapter 19

Deciding To Call A Doctor

The possibility that the intern might develop problems that do not respond to the techniques and resources reviewed in previous chapters deserves consideration. Basic medical strategy demands contingency plans for possible complications. This requires the development of criteria for the intern's decision to seek professional consultation for himself.

The Student's Health

To prepare for the stresses of internship, all health problems should be resolved to the maximum extent possible during medical school. Treatment of medical, surgical, orthopaedic, dental or psychiatric conditions can help bring the student into the best condition possible prior to the start of internship. Although the clinical years of medical school are demanding and time consuming, they allow much more latitude for obtaining thorough medical care than is the case during internship.

Well-conducted investigations have shown that a substantial number of medical students, as well as students in other graduate schools, use recreational drugs, some of them to the point of abuse. The prevalence of eating disorders, such as anorexia nervosa or bulimia nervosa, is substantial and appears to be increasing. At the same time, treatments for those conditions are improving. Medical, pharmacological and behavioral treatments can provide considerable relief. Self-help groups such as Alcoholics Anonymous, Overeaters Anonymous, or Drug Abusers Anonymous are highly effective as are groups devoted to other disorders that activate impulsive, uncontrolled, harmful behavior. They can be found in probably all cities in which medical schools are located.If the student has suffered from a recurrent disorder, he would do well to be prepared to resume treatment. It would be desirable to learn of effective treatment facilities or competent practitioners in the city in which the internship will be served. The intern's own hospital might not be the best place if special issues of confidentiality are involved.

Stress-Induced Symptoms

Even the large percentage of medical students who have not suffered either chronic or recurrent illnesses prior to internship can expect to experience symptoms, especially at the beginning. Anxiety, depression, difficulty in sleeping and irritability are symptoms that occur in many, if not all, interns at one time or another. Certainly extreme fatigue and sleep deprivation are universal. Usually these symptoms are transient. With the application of the methods discussed in this book, such as mental rehearsal, effective coping strategies, directed fantasies, autohypnosis and the others, symptoms are even more likely to be controlled or limited.

When symptoms arise they can usually be related to a current stress. Making such a connection can increase the intern's ability to manage his subjective condition and to reduce the dysphoria. It may lead to a release of encysted emotion. It may even point to burdens that can be shared or temporarily set aside or to circumstances that can be altered.

Insufficiently Processed Emotions

Two common sources of symptoms may not be recognized. The first is distress related to recent events that the intern had to ignore or chose to suppress. An example would be a particularly gruesome emergency situation, say the result of an automobile accident. The intern may have been so busy dealing with the treatment of the trauma that he was not able to react emotionally. Another example is the death of a patient that was poignant but was followed so quickly with other duties with other desperately ill patients, that the intern did not have the opportunity to pay attention to his feelings of grief. A third example is a disturbing event in the intern's personal life, such as news of illness in someone close and important. The intern may have thought, "I can't allow myself to get involved in that, because I have to get some sleep. I'm going to be on call tomorrow night."

Revival of Dysphoric Events

The second major source of mysteriously aroused symptoms if the reactivation of disturbing experiences from the past. Sometimes a common event in the hospital may revive in the intern turbulent emotions that were aroused at an earlier time. An example might be hearing about the diagnosis of cancer of the colon in a patient that might echo the same news about the intern's father. It may revive grief that had not been fully worked through about his father; it might arouse anxiety as the intern's mental apparatus tries to keep those awful personal memories out of consciousness; or it might produce insomnia, impairing the precious few hours that the intern has for sleep.

A battered child might evoke recall of his own experience as a victim of abuse.

When symptoms arise and the intern is not able to connect them with recent or remote stresses, two additional techniques may help him to discover the source. They are free association and directed association, described in the previous chapter.

Recognition of Symptoms Within

It is sometimes difficult for the intern to recognize an experience in himself as a symptom. Numerous psychiatric syndromes arise gradually and insidiously. They are manifested by changes in attitudes, perceptions and responses in ways that may not be clearly recognized from within as symptoms. An objective professional may be able to discern them more clearly when the intern describes his experiences. Depression, for example, is often accompanied by sleep disturbances and loss of interest in activities that were formerly or are currently of considerable significance. This can include a loss of ability to experience pleasure that may even grow to encompass sexual experiences.

Dysphoria is highly subjective and variable. It may be experienced as pain, dullness, weariness, despair, hopelessness, or relative immobility. It may be accompanied by feelings of blame, self-reproach, intense sense of inadequacy, or feelings of unworthiness. Energy to accomplish tasks is diminished. Concentration may be impaired. Memory, judgment and the capacity to learn and to apply knowledge to new experiences may be reduced. Appetite may increase or decrease significantly with corresponding changes in weight. There may be a slowing of physical activity or, paradoxically, hyperactivity may come in spurts.

Most ominous is the consideration of suicide. This may take the form of occasional thoughts of dying, wishes to die, desires to have something lethal occur to the intern. Even worse are plans or fantasies in which the intern finds a satisfying or desirable way of ending his own life.

Probably most interns experience some of these symptoms to at least a moderate degree in response to the exceptional stresses to which they are subjected. If these experiences persist, worsen or interfere noticeably with personal or professional functioning, an evaluation by a psychiatrist should be sought.

Anxiety disorders tend to be less insidious. They may appear in discreet episodes or attacks. Frequently they are manifested by autonomic discharge such as sweating, palpitations, rapid pulse, nausea, diarrhea, chest pain, fears of losing control, or fears or dying. Many of the foregoing symptoms are experienced by most interns. They are common responses to some of the emergency situations that the intern is required to confront. Feeling irritable, anxious, nervous or keyed up are frequent experiences. Difficulties in concentrating may be manifestations of anxiety as well as of depression. Difficulty in falling asleep or staying asleep, even when not on call, are common symptoms of anxiety. If these symptoms persist or worsen, then a clinical problem may well be present. (see Table 19.1)

Disorders of behavior are more easily recognized in one's self. Eating disorders are hard to ignore. Use of any psychoactive substance not prescribed by another physician is a matter of concern in people as seriously stressed as are most interns. The social use of alcohol may gradually increase in the internship year. It may be used as a form of self-medication to help with sleep or to counteract some of the symptoms of depression or anxiety listed earlier. Self-prescribed anxiolytics, sedatives or stimulants should signal caution from the first dose. The second dose may well signal danger (see Table 19.2).

Intrapsychic, interpersonal and psychophysiologic symptoms are more difficult to recognize because they often arise slowly and gradually and at some points are indistinguishable from appropriate and healthy responses to extremely stressful situations. Recognition of psychiatric syndromes in one's self is further confounded because the etiology may not be exclusively situational. It is well known that numerous medical and surgical disorders can be manifested by psychiatric symptoms initially. Examples are hyper- and hypothyroid conditions and brain tumors. Side effects of many prescription medications, such as benzodiazepines, as well as over-the counter drugs, such as anticholinergics, produce mental and emotional adverse symptoms. Psychoactive drugs and medications, of course, produce a spectrum of psychiatric side effects. Any or all of these, combined with the stresses of internship, can produce psychiatric syndromes. Some of them are relatively directly managed, for example, by removing the offending drug or treating the underlying medical or surgical condition. Management of others may be considerably more difficult.

Reticence to Seek Consultation

Interns, residents and other physicians tend to resist seeking consultation for problems of personal adaptation. Many are reluctant even to seek medical care for ailments short of those which grossly impair their functioning. They continue to work while in pain, injured or ill.

The resistance of physicians to become patients has multiple sources. Many physicians take great pride in their autonomy. They may perceive the patient's role as an indication of personal weakness.

Numerous interns fear impeding their own careers by acknowledging psychiatric problems or even difficulties in adapting to the stresses of internship. They fear that they will not be accepted by their own department.

Unfortunately, some departments are, in fact, intolerant of interns who admit to having problems. Such intolerance was far more prevalent in the past. Increasingly, teaching hospitals and their individual services are more aware of the problems that interns experience in the training process. The debate about working conditions for all residents has become more widespread. Studies, task forces, and even legislative action have become involved in the issue of sleep deprivation and other stressful factors in internship. This has led so far to relatively little change in working conditions but to a trend toward greater awareness, compassion and helpfulness on the part of training faculties. They have become more receptive to considering the problem and more willing to provide assistance to interns whose capacity for assimilating stress has been exceeded.

Despite these changes in attitude of the staffs of teaching hospitals, interns generally remain hesitant to seek outside assistance. Some of this fearfulness is based upon actual intolerance, some on the intern's own fears, and some on the intense ambition that a young physician may harbor. Many interns are burdened by a punitive inner demand for some sort of perfection or invincibility. These attitudes call for autognosis and attenuation.

Under some circumstances, the intern himself may not be able to soften the inner directed harshness. Unattainably strict personal standards accompanied by severe guilt, self-punishment or shame for failing to exemplify perfection, may be intensified by the stress of the work resulting in impairment.

Interns may also hesitate to ask for professional help because shame is wedded to the symptoms themselves. People suffering from bulimia nervosa are characteristically ashamed of their symptomatic behavior. This is true, also, of many people suffering from alcohol abuse or abuse of cocaine or narcotics.

Clear recognition of the resistances can serve as a significant step toward resolving them. Once the resistance is clearly defined in the intern's own mind, he is in a better position to sort out the consequences of seeking help and of avoiding it. Even in those increasingly rare situations in which training departments are genuinely intolerant of the personal problems experienced by interns, a way can be found to obtain necessary professional assistance without exposing it to the faculty. Consultation can be sought with a capable and trustworthy psychiatrist not affiliated with the teaching hospital. In situations in which patient care has not been compromised, such avoidance of unfavorable departmental attitudes can be a reasonable solution.

While obtaining professional help may be costly in time, money and dread, the rewards can be significant. As in making decisions about patient care, the risks and benefits need to be examined, evaluated and compared. In this instance, the intern is a patient, or a potential patient, and deserves at least that much consideration. The object of all of this is to enable the intern to become a better physician and to repair any temporary damage to this person who serves humanity and who will advance the tradition of the medical profession. Another important goal is protection of the people that the intern holds dear.

References

American Psychiatric Association: Diagnostic and Statistical Manual of Mental Disorders (3rd ed., revised [DSM-III-R]). Washington DC, American Psychiatric Association, 1987.

Baldwin DC Jr, Hughes PH, Conard SE, et al: Substance use among senior medical students. JAMA 1991;265:2074-2078.

Borenstein DB: Availability of mental health resources for residents in academic medical centers. J Med Educ 1985;60:517-523.

Borenstein DB: Should physician training centers offer formal psychiatric assistance to house officers? A report on the major findings of a prototype program. Am J Psychiatry 1985;142:1053-1057.

Clark DC, Zeldow PB: Vicissitudes of depressed mood during four years of medical school. JAMA 1988;260:2521-2528.

Craig AG, Pitts FN: Suicide by Physicians. Dis Nerv Syst 1968;29:763-772.

Fawcett J: Predictors of early suicide: Identification and appropriate intervention. J Clin Psychiatry 1988;49(10 suppl):7-8.

Fintzy RT: Psychiatric help for house officers. Am J Psychiatry 1986;143:273-274.

Hsu K, Marshall V: Prevalence of depression and distress in a large sample of Canadian residents, interns, and fellows. Amer J Psychiatry 1987;144:1561-1565.

Huebner LA, Royer JA, Moore J: The assessment and remediation of dysfunctional stress in medical school. J Med Educ 1981;56:547-558.

Hughes PH, Conard SE, Baldwin DC Jr, et al: Resident physician substance use in the United States. JAMA 1991;265:2069-2073.

Hurwitz TA, Beiser M, Nichol H, et al: Impaired interns and residents. Can J Psychiatry 1987;32:165-169.

Jensen PS: Barriers to working with impaired trainees: a resident's viewpoint. Psychiatr Q 1983;55:268-271.

Lloyd C, Gartrell NK: Psychiatric symptoms in medical students. Compr Psychiatry 1984;25:552-565.

Loes MW, Scheiber SC: The impaired resident. Ariz Med 1981;38:777-779.

Merril JM, Laux LF, Thornby JI, et al: Depression in medical students. JAMA 1989;261:2065-2066.

Reuben DB: Depressive symptoms in medical house officers. Arch Intern Med 1985;145:286-288.

Rich CL, Pitts FN: Suicide by male physicians during a five year period. Am J Psychiatry 1976;136:1089-1090.

Salmons PH: Psychiatric illness in medical students. Br J Psychiatry 1983;143:505-508.

Scott CD, Hawk J, eds. Heal Thyself: The Health of Health Care Professionals. New York, Brunner Mazel, 1986.

Simon W: Suicide among physicians: prevention and postvention. Crisis 1986;7:1-13.

Smith JW, Denny WF, Witzke DB: Emotional impairment in internal medicine house staff. JAMA 1986;255:1155-1158.

US Department of Health and Human Services: International Classification of Diseases, Ninth Revision, Clinical Modification (3rd ed), (Vol I), [ICD-9-CM]. Washington DC, US Government Printing Office, 1989.

Valko RJ, Clayton PJ: Depression in internship. Dis Nerv Syst 1975;36:26-29.

Victoroff VM, My dear colleague: Are you considering suicide? JAMA 1985;254:3464-3466.

Waring EM: Psychiatric illness in physicians: A review. Compr Psychiatry 1974;15:519-530.

Watterson DJ: Psychiatric illness in the medical profession: Incidence in relation to sex and field of practice. Can Med Assoc J 1976;115:311-317.

Westermeyer J: Substance use rates among medical students and resident physicians. JAMA 1991;265:2110-2111.

TABLE 19.1 – Symptoms to be Evaluated Professionally

- Sleep disturbances when not on call
- Apathy
- Anhedonia
- Despair
- Impaired concentration
- Excessive failures of memory
- Diminished ability to learn
- Suicidal ideation including wishes to die
- Intrusive thoughts
- Persistent autonomic symptoms
- Acquisition of extraordinary powers or knowledge
- Unexplained persistent extremes of mood

TABLE 19.2 – Signs to be Evaluated Professionally

- Uncharacteristic outbursts of emotion such as crying
- Repeated use of self-prescribed psychoactive substances
- Impairment of ability to work
- Disturbances or disruptions of significant personal relationships
- Violent behavior
- Suggestions by two or more friends, relatives or colleagues that help be sought
- Weight gain or loss greater than usual

Chapter 20

Summary

The stressfullness of postgraduate medical education has been well documented. Institutional responses to reduce pressures on residents have been discussed in the news media, medical schools, state legislatures, hospital boards, and elsewhere. Many recommendations have been made and a few have been instituted to reduce sleep deprivation and to improve supervision. Despite all of the discussion and publication, there has been a scarcity of literature on individual responses designed to reduce stress or to enhance resilience among resident physicians. This work offers a menu of methods for strengthening adaptive capacity which the individual can use.

1. Morbidity, including family disruption, substance abuse, depression and suicide, resulting from the stresses of postgraduate medical education has been reported. Even more widespread have been effects of decreased morale, disillusionment, and misanthropy. Anticipation and preparation can help. Common challenges contributing to the difficulties are: responsibility for patient care, emergencies, nights without sleep, AIDS, and malpractice litigation. Some of these factors can also add to the richness, excitement, and intensity of the opportunity to treat patients in emergencies or patients suffering from dreadful diseases. Sleepless nights sometimes result in learning from continuous care of patients.

2. A method already familiar to residents is mental rehearsal: playing out an expected situation in one's mind. Students are accustomed to focusing on facts or events, for example, in examinations or interviews. Residents can also focus on the expected emotional reactions and the interpersonal aspects of what they anticipate. They can learn to extend the scene to what happens next. For example, a resident might try to play through mentally what happens following the immediate observation and initial treatment of an emergency or of violence, or following a humiliating situation.

3. Clinicians know the usefulness of history-taking. Residents can apply this to their own experience and examine responses to stresses they have experienced in the past. They can delineate the coping strategies they have used in response to acute and to chronic challenges. They may evaluate effectiveness and cost and sort the useful strategies from those that were counterproductive. Residents can decide to avoid the ones that were ineffective. Through observation of other people who faced comparable stresses they may add new strategies and upgrade their repertoire.

4. Under stress, perspective, judgment and cognition may be impaired or overcome by intense emotion. On the other hand, feelings can be drowned in a flood of racing thoughts. Learning to observe and to assess variations in intensity of thought and feeling can prevent insidious reduction of effectiveness of either of those important personal functions. Volitional creation of an inner dialogue can be useful in retaining awareness of what is transpiring in the internal space. Skillful choice of the speakers in this internal conversation can add to the effectiveness of the procedure.

5. Our ability to compose and direct the contents of imagination can be employed in other tasks. Expressive fantasies can be used to decompress intense surges of emotion such as anger, fear or sadness. Rehearsal fantasies can help us prepare for difficult interpersonal encounters. Performance fantasies can complement practice to sharpen skills in preparation for medical procedures. Central to the usefulness of expressive fantasies is the recognition that they are distinct from the corresponding actions and need not be enacted.

6. Constructively channeled actions can serve to discharge frustration, anger and other products of stress. Opportunities for athletics tend to be limited during residency, but substitutes can be created with available facilities. Fitness can be maintained with procedures such as stair climbing and isometrics and reinforced with sound nutrition. Sexual behavior has multiple benefits and risks.

7. Despite recurrent or chronic sleep deprivation, residents often suffer from insomnia. Tension, over-stimulation or depression may contribute to impaired sleep, even on nights off. Abuse of sedatives is a consequent risk. Harmless, effective and readily available alternatives are techniques for relaxation and for autohypnosis.

8. Preparation of family and friends can help prevent some of the disappointments and conflicts that can further undermine the resident's resilience. The resident's physical and emotional unavailability can strain relationships that might otherwise be nurturing. If discussed in advance, procedures can be devised that can actually reinforce the bonds of mutuality.

9. Affection, respect and comradeship can be sources of strength. Individual virtues such as compassion, honesty and perseverance deserve to be noticed and appreciated by the resident himself and brought to bear in meeting challenges. Accomplishments can be recalled and relished. Awareness of one's specific sensitivies can be useful in preparing for difficult circumstances. Recognition of both strengths and vulnerabilities can lead to better adaptation and reduction of pain. Comparable perspectives on beneficial and detrimental relationships can prove rewarding.

10. In difficult circumstances, mementoes of happier times can improve morale. Those times need first to be identified. Connections can be established through memory as well as through people, places, things and activities. Savoring them in the present can offer comfort and cultivate hope.

11. Misbehavior by patients can complicate their care and can add burdens on the resident. Cultivation of collaborative relationships with patients can reduce conflicts in some instances. Taking note of the patient's individuality can sometimes weave a bond with the clinician.

    A useful hypothesis regarding patients' misbehavior is that is may be a form of communication. The resident's subjective response may be a source of clinical data in deciphering the message. Objective data, including reports from other informants, can validate, refute or modify the hypothesis. Translation of the significance of the behavior into words can facilitate clinical management.

    Phenomena such as hospital discharge reactions, disruptive conduct, threats and violence often require special measures. Understanding a patient's deeper concerns can be crucial.

12. Fellow residents can lighten each other's burdens professionally and emotionally. Temporary disability of one member, especially of the interns' class, can add substantially to the clinical load of all the others. Maternity is a special kind of temporary disability and can raise complex problems. Conflicts, especially between interns, can be troublesome and need to be resolved with care and maturity.

13. Postgraduate medical education is a hierarchical apprenticeship. Beginning residents learn from those with more experience. Elders teach techniques for getting things done and for coping with the challenges of training, along with the essentials of medicine or surgery. Most senior house officers and attendings are helpful but some are abusive. Many medical students are subjected to abuse and may have learned methods to enable them to cope with it. It is a shameful feature of medical education that must be overcome by the individual and expunged by the profession.

14. A hospital is a complex system requiring workers with various skills and occupations. A resident will encounter many employees who can facilitate or impede his work. Courteous, considerate behavior is usually rewarded with help and a more pleasant ambiance. Excessive intimacy can produce costly problems for the resident and for others.

15. Residents work at an intensity so high that it may leave little energy for social life, family responsibilities and other interests. Unexpected events, such as illness or death of a family member, place an even greater strain on the house officer than they would on someone in a less demanding occupation. Life presents us all with events over which we have no control. Yet, prior thought given to the circumstances of all who are important to the resident may lead to effective preventive measures in some instances. Mental rehearsal and planning can reduce distress and increase effectiveness if an accident or tragedy occurs.

16. Hospitals are entities that require multiple systems to enable them to deal with myriad events internally and with related individuals and agencies. Requirements of these systems sometimes distract the resident from the immediate concerns of patient care. The institution and its bureaucracy

may then become a target of much of the frustration and anger built up in the heat of training. Such feelings can be misleading and may override good judgement. In some instances, skill in dealing with the organization can benefit patients. Ethical dilemmas arise in many aspects of residency training but are especially keen in relation to limited resources — both human and institutional.

17. In their late 20's and early 30's, residents face major personal choices. They may be forming a committed relationship or a family. They face choices of where to live after training and what sort of practice to enter. The time constraints of residency, emotional overload, and depletion of resources may undermine judgment. Basic principles of decision-making may be ignored. Consideration of goals, aversions, antecedents and alternatives may be slighted. Available data may be insufficient and review and consultation may be bypassed.

18. Most techniques for building resilience focus on what is readily available to consciousness, what is rational and what are familiar perceptions. If residents suspend temporarily the requirement to be logical and relevant and allow themselves to observe the contents of their minds, they may reach new insights. Free associations may lead them to ideas, feelings, attitudes and perceptions that were formerly outside of their awareness. Spontaneous and even directed associations may energize perceptiveness, intuition and creativity.

19. Combinations of factors may produce psychological symptoms or signs of impairment that do not respond to the methods described in this book. Some medical and surgical conditions are initially manifested by psychiatric symptoms. Stress-induced symptoms and insufficiently processed emotions may take their toll. Distressing events from the past may be re-experienced with all their attendant dysphoria. Current stress may trigger major depression or one of the anxiety disorders. If the resident suspects that a professional consultation could add objectivity and expertise to clarify his own distress, it would be well to seek it. The resident's responsibility to his loved ones, his patients and

his colleagues urges that he do whatever he can to prevent worsening of his own condition. Perhaps most important, even young doctors deserve proper care.

20. People who are able to complete medical school have proven themselves resilient. Postgraduate medical education may challenge their fortitude as much as, or more than, any previous experience. Additional adaptive competence can be developed using their own mental and emotional resources as suggested in this book. Many techniques and procedures described can be employed beneficially in life beyond residency. More than warding off impairment and suffering, they might make more accessible satisfaction and joy.